CW00821482

NEJANG

TIBETAN SELF-HEALING YOGA

Dr. Nida Chenagtsang

SKY
PRESS

Medical Disclaimer

This book is not intended for the purpose of providing medical advice. All information, content, and material in this book is for informational purposes only and is not intended to serve as a substitute for the consultation, diagnosis, and/or medical treatment of a qualified physician or healthcare provider.

Cover: Lukhang Mural photography © Thomas Laird LLC, 2018

A detail from a mural in the Lukhang temple in Lhasa, depicting Tibetan yogis engaging in *lüjong trulkhor* physical yoga exercises. This temple, dedicated to the *lu* or water spirits, was built by the fifth Dalai Lama in the seventeenth century on a small island located in a pond behind the Potala Palace, to serve as a private chapel and yoga and meditation space for his lineage.

Published by:

Sky Press

Pure Land Farms
3265 Santa Maria Road
Topanga, CA 90290

www.skypressbooks.com

Copyright © 2020 by Nida Chenagtsang
རྒྱལ་སྤྱིའི་བོད་ཀྱི་གསོ་རིག་ཁང་།
www.sorig.net

ISBN: 9781950153039

Editor: Christiana Polites and Ben Joffe
Design and Typesetting: Pearse Gaffney
Nejang Yoga Graphic Images: Nisha J
Nejang Yoga Photography: Ludovic Basset
First English Edition
Printed on acid-free paper

Special thanks to all whose valuable contributions
made this work possible.

Contents

Prefaces

Introduction

Chapter One: Energetic Body

Chapter Two: Health Benefits of Nejang

Chapter Three: The Preliminaries

Chapter Four: The Actual Practice

Conclusion

Appendices

Prefaces

Preface by Author - Dr. Nida Chenagtsang

Foreword by Professor Robert Thurman

Foreword by Editor - Christiana Polites

A Note on Tibetan Terminology

"Life is about being the original and organic you!"

- Dr. Nida Chenagtsang

Author's Preface

Today yoga has become very popular, one of the most important Asian traditions which has crossed into the West. I think this is very good, because yoga should be a universal science that can benefit all. Of course there are some very secret yogas and ones that require very intensive and strict spiritual trainings for advanced practitioners, but it's important to know that there are many different kinds of yoga. In Tibet, for example we have *Lujong* and *Tsa Loong Trulkhor*; and all the different Tantric schools describe different yogas in their traditional texts. Most of the practices are highly secret in Tibet, these are yogas with higher goals whose main purpose is to bring the practitioner to enlightenment. I call these the 'professional' yogas — these ones cannot be taught to the general public because of the intensive trainings they require, and even if they could be taught publicly they would not be useful for most people. But there are also other types of yoga which are more for physical exercise or some that are focused on healing, such as the Nejang Yoga taught in this book. It's true that Nejang comes originally from the Kalachakra Tantra so we cannot say that it is only for healing; it is also a deep spiritual practice that aims to purify the channels and give the practitioner access to the pure dimensions. But for the general public, it can be a very beneficial healing practice and for this reason it should be taught openly and made very accessible.

For the past decade at least I have been teaching this Nejang Yoga to both my students and my patients and I have seen directly how well the exercises work due to their simplicity and practical applications. A variety of different issues can be directly addressed by these twenty four exercises. One of the main problems and causes of health concerns in our modern society is a sedentary lifestyle, but to counter this sedentary lifestyle it is not always necessary to do extreme or rigorous sports. Even very simple movements such as turning the head, moving the joints or doing self-massage like in this yoga can help dramatically. It's very useful for elderly people who lack mobility in certain parts of their body, and even little kids love this yoga and benefit from it, finding it fun and inspiring. I have seen for myself how practical and useful Nejang can be for so many kinds of people of all ages which is why I am very committed to teaching and spreading this practice widely.

We should know that drugs and medications including herbal remedies are not the only solutions for resolving medical issues — it is also beneficial to use external therapies such as massage or moxa, and very important to work to improve our lifestyle through techniques such as yoga, physical exercise, and breathing. Just as medical associations now recognize the Chinese practices of tai chi and chi gong as real medical treatments, I really hope that Nejang will also be recognized one day as a kind of medical treatment. Once people recognize its health benefits and can feel its effects on both body and mind, it can also serve as a bridge for entering into the spiritual dimensions of practice, thereby bringing even deeper benefits.

Dr. Nida Chenagtsang
Sorig Khang International
www.sorig.net

Foreword by Professor Robert Thurman

What I love about Dr. Nida's work is that it's so real, down-to-earth, appropriate, courageous and straightforward. He always achieves that because he lives, and so draws directly from, the precious web of Tibetan Buddhistic culture, which interacts so creatively with the variety of contemporary cultures.

Why is that culture so special? In a sense all indigenous earth and sky nature-oriented cultures are special in these days dominated by the industrial-strength alienation of the dominant materialist culture of the planet. But among these many precious cultures, Tibetan culture holds a special place, because it is the most mainstream "buddhicized" culture of all. There are a number of heavily Buddhism-influenced nations, but Buddhism occupies a "counter-cultural" space within them. This is easy to determine. When the dominant institution in a society is the military, with a king or nowadays a president as the commander in chief, the Buddhist communities and their principles of freedom, nonviolence, wisdom, and compassion, are only counter-cultural, serving as a restraining influence on the violence-oriented mainstream culture.

In the case of Tibet, from around 600CE to 1600 CE, the Indic Buddhist educational enterprise enabled its society to undergo a near-total transformation from a militarized conquest empire culture to a demilitarized (i.e. "monasticized") culture devoted to the pursuit of enlightenment, defined as wise (attuned to the relativity of the universe experienced as beneficial to sentient life), compassionate (sensitive to and engaged with the life project of altruistically helping other beings free themselves from suffering), and joyfully and energetically creative, feeling supported by loving and powerful supernormal beings in making their human lives fully meaningful and beautiful for themselves and others.

How do the Nejang exercises manifest the mainstream "buddhified" culture of Tibet? These exercises, like the Hatha Yoga exercises of India, but with a visceral earthiness edge, are especially liberating for the individual person. They nudge her or him to take responsibility for his or her own health, well-being, and cheerful attitude. Here you learn to pull and twist your own nose, to stimulate your lungs, etc. You purse your lips and stretch them out, expanding your jaw muscles, to stimulate your spleen, and loosen the gripping jaw clenching attitudes of fear and rigid control that cause grinding teeth during sleep when the stress of life is experienced as distressing, just too much. You rub your own neck and pull your ears to prevent ossification in your hearing channels to stay open to what's happening around you. In general you tune your body, outside and inside, to reflect your confidence and ease in allowing your body to serve you well to interconnect positively with the sensitive environment of other beings and natural elements. Enlightened beings, buddhas of various kinds, see the human being and its long well-adapted environment as a blissful play of beautifully mutual energies, in contrast to the barely adequate realm of insufficiency and hopeless struggle that we, as misknowing, unrealized beings, experience in subliminal or vocal desperation.

This need not be our fate. We can take back control of our bodies and our days and nights. Learning and developing habits based on the self-knowledge inculcated by the practice of Nejang is a big step toward feeling better, more well, more capable, and more free. Start caring for your body as if it were one of the favorite stuffed animals you used to play with and cuddle with as a child! Enjoy this little book on Nejang, Tibet's gift to you of a basic self-care operating instruction manual!

Tenzin Bob Thurman
Professor Emeritus, Buddhist scholar, author,
and ongoing practitioner

Editor's Foreword

I'm very honored to publish this long awaited book on a little-known, but tremendously beneficial form of Tibetan yoga, called Nejang. Studying this profound practice with Dr. Nida Chenagtsang has been a natural progression and deepening of a several decade-long personal journey with yoga. I first encountered both yoga and Buddhism when I was fifteen years old, in a history class on world religions in which my teacher introduced us not only to the theory but also to the living practices of the traditions we studied. Immediately attracted to the simple meditations and yoga postures he taught us, I embarked on my own path, attending daily yoga classes at the end of my high school day in New York City, just when yoga was beginning to become popularized amongst the artists and hipsters of the East Village, but long before it entered the mainstream American consciousness as it has today. The combination of rigorous physical exercises, breathwork, and meditation along with an introduction to the philosophies of ancient India opened my troubled teenager mind, improved my health and drastically changed the entire course of my life.

Two decades later, after deep immersions into Tibetan Vajrayana Buddhism and having embarked on a path of studying Chinese and alternative medicines, I met Dr. Nida Chenagtsang and learned the twenty four Nejang yoga exercises that are taught in this book. Less attracted to the extremely athletic forms of yoga that I did religiously in my younger years and much more interested in learning how to tap into deeper states of healing and awareness through body and energy practices, this Nejang Yoga was a perfect gift. The gentleness and simplicity of the exercises makes them easily integratable into any daily routine. Whether one has five minutes or one hour to dedicate to this practice, the effect on both body and mind can be immediately felt. Nejang can be done in a very slow and relaxed way to cultivate greater calmness in the mind, or it can be practiced in a faster more vigorous manner to generate heat and open the channels, which produces a much more energizing effect. In this way the practice is very flexible and adaptable to one's personal needs and circumstances making it easy to teach and share with others. Whether you are a yoga teacher, massage therapist, acupuncturist, or working in any field of healing or medicine, this is a wonderful way to directly benefit yourself, your patients, and your students.

In a day and age when mainstream studio yoga has become associated with super fit and youthful bodies and contortionism, Nejang Yoga is a most welcome addition to this modern yoga 'scene'. Dr. Nida's instructions on the Nejang exercises are paired with foundational teachings on Tibetan medicine, subtle anatomy, and simple teachings on the Kalachakra Tantra (the 'Wheel of Time' scripture) that connect the twenty four 'places' or locations of the body (Tibetan: *né* གནས།) that we 'train' or 'purify' (Tibetan: *jang* སྦྱང་།) with the twenty four outer and inner sacred tantric dimensions. Contemplating these deeper teachings as I do Nejang yoga brings these seemingly simple exercises to life, making it a practice that can never become boring and that unfolds and deepens increasingly the more I do it.

I'm very grateful to have received this precious instruction from Dr. Nida, to have had the opportunity to teach it to others and share its benefits, and to work with him to publish this book with Sky Press. All of the information contained in this book comes directly from Dr. Nida's instruction, derived from transcripts and the may teachings, both formal and informal, that I have received from him on this and other topics over the years. While there is much more that could be written about the powerful effects of the movements and breathwork of this yoga from the perspective of modern Western science and medicine, we have chosen to focus mostly on the traditional Tibetan perspective. The exception to this is the inclusion of several anatomical images to illustrate the muscles activated through these practices which helps to illuminate the many levels at which this simple practice can affect the body, both energetically and physically.

I sincerely hope that the information contained here will inspire people to learn, practice, and share this yoga, so that it may spread and bring benefit to people of all ages, spiritual backgrounds, and physical conditions all over the world. I would like to thank all those whose valuable contributions helped to bring this book to fruition, most especially to Ben Joffe (*Jigme Dorje*) for his Tibetan translations and tireless support in editing, to Pearse Gaffney for graphics and layout, and to Nisha J for her illustrations of the twenty four exercises which so accurately show these movements that are at times difficult to describe in words.

This book is a guide and is not intended to replace direct instruction from a qualified teacher. To find Nejang Yoga teachers and courses in your country, please visit Sorig Khang International: Foundation for Traditional Tibetan Medicine at **www.sorig.net**.

Christiana Polites
Sky Press & Pure Land Farms
www.skypressbooks.com
www.purelandfarms.org

A Note on Tibetan Terminology

It was Dr. Nida's wish that this Nejang book (just like the yoga itself) be accessible to people of varying interests and backgrounds. For this reason, we limited our use of Tibetan terms and attempted wherever possible to use common English language. Nevertheless, in order to preserve the integrity of the larger system of Tibetan spiritual practices to which Nejang belongs, we have included key Tibetan terminology wherever it seemed necessary or appropriate. When Tibetan terms appear, we have chosen to use a simple phonetic transliteration rather than the Wylie system of transliteration that is difficult to read and pronounce for those unfamiliar with Tibetan Studies. Tibetan phonetic terms appear throughout the text in italics. Only very key terms appear in Tibetan script when they are first mentioned. The word Nejang is not italicized due to its frequent recurrence. In order to distinguish Sanskrit from Tibetan terminology, Sanskrit words have been left unitalicized. We have also left diacritic marks of Sanskrit terms. Original translations of Butön Rinchen Drup's text and additional Tibetan sources included in this book were done by Ben Joffe *(Jigme Dorje)*.

Introduction: The Meaning of Yoga

Yoga Today & The Meaning of Yoga
in the Tibetan Tradition

Body, Energy, and Mind: Nejang Yoga
and the Continuum Between
Spiritual and Physical Cultivation

Nejang for Everyone: Yoga as Medicine

"Beneath your stress and confusion there is unconditional love for everyone. Each time you meditate you uncover this love."

- Dr. Nida Chenagtsang

Introduction

Yoga Today and the Meaning of Yoga in the Tibetan Tradition

Today yoga is popular all over the world. People from many different backgrounds currently practice physical yogic exercises and breathing techniques derived more or less directly from Indian traditions. They practice these both alone at home and in groups at yoga studios to improve their health, physical strength, and fitness, and to reduce stress and aid relaxation. As Indian styles of yoga have become more accepted globally, more and more people have become convinced of yoga's positive impact on mental and physical wellbeing. Yet despite the popularity of yoga for physical health today, many people are not familiar with the deeper meaning of yoga or with the diversity of yoga practices that exist. One aspect of yogic practice with which many people are unfamiliar is Tibet's traditions of healing yoga.

There are many reasons why Tibetan yoga traditions are less well-known and understood. On the one hand, a strong focus on Indian yoga's usefulness for health and wellbeing has at times resulted in a downplaying of yoga's spiritual roots and meaning. In Tibet, yoga is very connected with the practice of Buddhism, and esoteric Buddhism in particular. Historically, Tibetan yogic disciplines have been pursued by religious specialists or professionals as part of dedicated religious practice, often in the context of extended spiritual retreats. Many Tibetan yogic practices aimed at manipulating and transforming the human body, energy, and mind have been quite secret and restricted. Traditionally, Tibetan yogis and yoginis (male and female practitioners of yoga) have become initiated into particular lineages or schools of spiritual practice and have learned yogic techniques directly from the gurus and texts of their lineage. These texts are sometimes hard to understand without supplementary guidance from teachers and fellow practitioners. As a result of these factors, Tibetan yoga traditions have been much less accessible to the broader public.

Many people are surprised to learn that Tibet has its own traditions of physical or postural yoga. While they have heard about Indian style asanas and stretching and breathing exercises which derive broadly from India's ancient Hatha Yoga traditions, they are less familiar with parallel Tibetan practices found in esoteric or tantric Buddhism and Bön religion. Sometimes people have heard about other Tibetan yoga practices like Dream Yoga which involves learning to be lucid and to gain control in the dreaming state, or Deity Yoga, where one trains to perceive oneself as an enlightened Buddhist deity. There is also Guru Yoga, a key aspect of all tantric Buddhism or Vajrayana. This involves supplicating and meditating on one's spiritual teacher in the form of a Buddha until one gains confidence in the fact that there is no difference between one's own seemingly ordinary mind, the mind of one's teacher, and that of a Buddha. Some people have also heard about special Tibetan yogas performed in preparation for and during death, or about the Yoga of Inner Heat or *tummo* where yogis and yoginis generate great warmth and bliss in their bodies[1]. Today there is also growing interest in Karmamudra or Tibetan practices of tantric sexual yoga, the yoga of bliss in which ordinary desires and cravings are transformed into limitless, unconditional bliss beyond any sense of self-or-other[2].

These practices all have the name 'yoga' but at first sight they seem quite different from one another, and quite different from the quite casual and secular-seeming physical or 'corporate' yoga practices many people do during the week at the gym. But if we really understand the deeper meaning of yoga then it will be easy for us to see the continuity between physical yoga practices that promote health and wellbeing and more esoteric spiritual practices which teach us about the nature of our human consciousness, and which can be used as powerful methods for achieving enlightenment in and through our human body.

'Yoga' is a Sanskrit word which is commonly translated into English as 'to join' or 'unite'. The idea here is that the diverse methods or spiritual disciplines of yoga, whatever specific form they may take, all share a common aim or ultimate purpose – namely, the goal of uniting oneself with the divine or original source, of returning one's relative, limited, or fragmented self to its basic nature. The Tibetan translation of the Sanskrit word 'yoga' is *naljor* (རྣལ་འབྱོར།). *Nal* (short for *nalma*) means the pure, primordial, original, or uncontrived state, and *jor* (short for *jorwa*) means 'to receive, to arrive at, or to connect with'. Like the true meaning of the original Sanskrit word yoga, *naljor* refers to any method which has the aim of bringing the practitioner back to their primordial, unconditioned, and uncontaminated true nature. According to Buddhist teachings, from the ultimate perspective, our primordial, pure state can never be stained or damaged. It is with and within

---

1. Dream Yoga (Milam, རྨི་ལམ།) and Tummo Yoga (གཏུམ་མོ།) are two of the famous 'Six Yogas' or 'Dharmas' of Naropa, the celebrated eleventh century Indian tantric yogic master or mahasidda ('great accomplished one') who initiated and trained great Tibetan Buddhist practitioners and thereby helped spread tantric Buddhist yoga practices from India in Tibet. The other four yogas are: Illusory (or Magic) Body Yoga (*gyülü*, སྒྱུ་ལུས།); Clear Light Yoga (*ösel*, འོད་གསལ།) connected with deep, dreamless sleep; Powa Yoga (འཕོ་བ།), the yoga of transference of consciousness at the moment of death, and Bardo Yoga (བར་དོ།), the yoga for traversing the intermediate state between death and rebirth.

---

2. To learn more about this topic, please read my book *Karmamudra: The Yoga of Bliss, Sexuality in Tibetan Medicine and Buddhism* (Chenagtsang, 2018).

us at all times, regardless of whether we are able to recognize and experience it or not. It is said that our true nature is just like a beautiful, indestructible, totally clear and radiant diamond that has somehow become covered in dirt, making it unrecognizable to the ordinary eye. The 'dirt' on the diamond is the accumulated patterns of our past actions, habitual tendencies, and mistaken perceptions – just like with the diamond, our true nature is in no way altered by the layer of grime, it has merely become obscured and must be scrubbed clean to reveal its innate value. In the Tibetan tradition, yoga is thus understood to be one of the most important methods for cleaning the diamond of our ultimate nature. Through yogic practice we train or purify ourselves in order to reveal our innately pure, clear, open, and luminous nature which has become hidden beneath layers of confusion.

Body, Energy, and Mind: Nejang Yoga and the Continuum Between Spiritual and Physical Cultivation

There are many different types of yoga in the Tibetan tradition, all of which aim to bring the yogini or yogi back to this original state. All these different practices are profound methods designed to engage every aspect of one's life and being for the purpose of transformation. Yogic practices transform our body, energy, and mind, they turn life and death itself into an opportunity for reawakening to and reuniting with our pure, primordial nature.

So far so good, but you may still be wondering what exactly physical exercises, stretching, breathwork, or special postures that improve bodily health have to do with this very lofty sounding goal. The yogic practices described in this book, which are known as Nejang (གནས་སྦྱངས་) literally meaning 'place purification' or 'purification of the abodes', are self-healing techniques that improve bodily, energetic, and mental wellbeing. Simple yet effective, they can be used by almost anyone. They make use of sequences of simple physical movements, self-massage, and breath cultivation techniques. As such, these Nejang exercises fall under the umbrella of what Tibetans call *lüjong* or *lüjong trulkhor* practices. *Lü* is the Tibetan word for 'body' while *jong* means 'purification', 'refinement' or 'training'[3]. *Trulkhor* is a little more complicated to render into English but can be literally translated as 'magic wheel' or 'magical machine'[4]. *Trulkhor* exercises involve series of physical movements involving breath and energy control and are the closest Tibetan practices to traditional Indian Hatha yoga techniques.

The 'magic wheel' in the name *trulkhor* sounds a little strange. Some scholars have proposed that the 'wheel' (*khor*) in *trulkhor* is in reference to the cycles or sequences of movements found in these practices, one dynamic movement flowing into the next like a revolving wheel. But we can think of *trulkhor* a little more broadly than that. *Trulkhor* ultimately refers to our own human potential to become something extraordinary. The 'magical wheel' or 'machine' in question is the microcosm of our own gross and subtle body, which in tantric Buddhism is the source of enlightenment itself. Our body arises from out of a miraculous set of moving, automated systems. These dynamic systems are impermanent and constantly changing. They appear as if by magic, seemingly from nowhere, yet they work together to make up our solid and stable seeming forms. Unlike some other spiritual traditions, tantric Buddhism does not claim that spiritual realization or freedom from suffering is found through denying or transcending the body. Instead, tantric yoga shows us how we can realize our ultimate nature through the here-

---

3. *Jong[wa]* is a slightly different form of the word '*jang*' found in Nejang.

---

4. In recent decades, *trulkhor* practices have also been popularized outside of Tibet by the great Tibetan master Chogyal Namkhai Norbu Rinpoche (1938 – 2018) under the Sanskrit title of Yantra Yoga. Yantra, which means machine or geometrical spiritual design, is one way to say *trulkhor* in Sanskrit.

and-now of our embodied human condition, through maximizing our potential. A machine is something that can enhance or streamline the natural, vital capacities of a human being. It takes something that we already have the potential to do but maximizes that potential, making us more powerful and efficient. Without that original human potential, the machine would not make sense or be able to function. Tantric yogic practices are thus 'magical machines' because they enhance and refine the magical potential of our human body, energy, and mind.

Another category of *trulkhor* in Tibetan is *tsa loong trulkhor* or 'the Magic Wheel exercises [that work with the] channels and winds'. Traditionally, more physical *lüjong* body training or purification exercises function as preliminary practices that prepare yoginis and yogis for the main *tsa loong trulkhor* practice. The channels and winds are key elements of tantric yogic subtle anatomy which will be addressed more fully in later sections of this book. *Trulkhor* exercises are understood to be one of the most direct and effective ways to work with and transform one's channels and winds. In Tibet, *tsa loong trulkhor* exercises were often undertaken as part of intensive retreats as preparation for learning *Tummo* or Inner Heat Yoga. As one of the Six Yogas, *tummo* involves both Guru and Deity Yoga practice, and is regarded as a Completion or Perfection Stage (*dzogrim*) practice in Tibetan Buddhism. *Tummo* is one of the most important and direct Tibetan practices for producing and mastering yogic heat, which forms the basis of many other yogic practices. Purifying, toning, and training the subtle energetic channels and winds provides a basis for generating heat and bliss, which in turn allows yoginis and yogis to perceive and rest in their ultimate nature.

Lüjong trulkhor exercises like Nejang are types of yogic practice that train the body and the breath so as to facilitate the balanced and unobstructed flow of the wind energies, to open the channels and the mind. They are explicitly about training and refining the body but their final aim and broader context of practice is about reuniting with our true nature. In tantric yoga, mind and body are inextricably connected. In Tibetan Buddhism and medicine, the 'three gates' or 'doors' (Tibetan, *go soom*) of body, energy, and mind *lü, ngak, took*) are understood to be one single continuum of being[5]. For this reason, utilizing these three dimensions of our being equally and together is a beneficial and necessary approach to realizing the results of yogic practice as swiftly as possible. As we will see later in this book in the chapter on subtle anatomy, our body contains a vast network of energy channels (*tsa*) in which wind energy (*loong*) flows. In most people's ordinary bodies, the channels are knotted and blocked so that the wind energy cannot flow freely. This in turn has a profound impact not only on our physical health and vitality but also on how we experience our mind. Blocked channels and congested, imbalanced energies prevent us from abiding in the non-dual state of pristine awareness, which is our natural state. Instead, we get caught up in dualistic and discursive thinking and perpetuate all the negative thought patterns that according to Buddhist teachings trap us in samsara, the cycle of life, death, and rebirth which is defined by suffering[6].

In keeping with the idea of body-energy-and-mind as a continuum, Tibetan Buddhism and medicine teaches that even though these negative thought patterns or 'poisons' are experienced by our mind, they are stored inside our subtle energy body, in the

---

5. In Vajrayana teachings it is more common to read of the triad 'body, speech, and mind.' In this book, however, we will be using the word 'energy' instead of 'speech' to translate the second term of this traditional concept. 'Speech' in the tantric Buddhist understanding of the word is related not only to language but to our *loong* or wind energy and breath as well, which is the underlying basis of spoken words and our capacity for communication and creation. In the context of yogic practice and health, the word 'energy' better conveys this concept.

five main chakras or energy centers (literally 'wheels', *khorlo* in Tibetan) that are located along our central channel. This notion is maybe a little reminiscent of current biomedical research about epigenetics and trauma that is inherited across generations, where mental and emotional trauma and responses are somehow stored in the cells of our physical body. It is also similar to ideas in various alternative healing systems which likewise posit that until we are able to free up some of the deep-rooted physical holding patterns that keep the experience of trauma trapped in our bodies, it can be difficult to release ourselves mentally from our suffering. This is why the most effective kinds of trauma therapies involve a combination of psychotherapy and somatic practices, which work with the body and breath.

Because our body, energy, and mind operate indivisibly, they are able to both help and harm one another. We can see many examples of this from our own everyday lives and experiences. Our speech and energy, as well as our mind, can be both aided and constrained by the body. For example, diseases of the nervous system can make some patients mute, and any number of bodily afflictions can disturb our mental wellbeing. At the same time, the power of the mind can influence our energy and body in negative

---

6. According to Buddhist teachings we have 84,000 mental afflictions. These can be condensed down to the five 'poisons' of confusion or ignorance; desire or attachment; anger or hatred; pride; and jealousy, which can be further condensed into the three primary poisons of confusion, desire, and anger. These three can then be condensed even further into the single, ultimate poison of ignorance, or 'un-knowing' (*marigpa* in Tibetan), the delusion or misapprehension of the nature of self and reality which is the root cause of all suffering. From the perspective of Tibetan Medicine, these poisons not only cause us to continuously cycle or wander in samsara but are also the ultimate origin of the three humors and thus the principal cause of the manifestation of sickness in our physical bodies. This will be explained in greater detail in subsequent chapters.

and positive ways as well. When our mind is heroic or proud the tone of our voice changes, it becomes higher and richer, and our body posture changes. When we feel defeated or are in pain, this is discernible in our voice and general energy as well: words catch in our throats, how we hold ourselves physically changes, and our complexion begins to look less vital and healthy. Our speech and energy too, can influence the body and mind. In Tibetan medicine it is taught that excessive talking can increase one's *loong* and as a result of this, wind diseases may arise or be exacerbated and make one's body and mind unwell. Harsh and hateful words can make our own and others' minds sick, and conversely, expressing pleasant words can gladden others' hearts. When it comes to psychotherapy, we can also communicate through words to treat various mental illnesses. These are common, everyday examples that most readers will probably find fairly uncontroversial. And yet even as we credit these possibilities, it is easy to forget the amazing consequences and opportunities provided by the inter-connectedness of our body-energy-and-mind. Tibetan yoga makes use of these opportunities, of this potential.

While it is possible to unblock the channels and chakras with the power of the mind alone, by using advanced meditation techniques, visualization, and concentration (or even to move beyond the apparent confines of the body altogether through the direct recognition of the nature of things associated with Ati Yoga or *Dzogchen* teachings[7]), this is very challenging. For most people, using physical yogas to unblock the channels is a more practical

---

7. Ati Yoga, 'The Extreme/Ultimate/Utmost' Yoga in Sanskrit, also known as *Dzogchen* or the 'Great Perfection' in Tibetan, is a set of profound, extremely precise meditation instructions for abiding in pure natural awareness. Readers who would like more information on Ati Yoga are invited to read my two books on the subject, *Mirror of Light* (Chenagtsang 2016) and *Weapon of Light* (Chenagtsang 2017).

and effective method, one which slowly but steadily unlocks deeper levels of awareness and expands our capacity to do higher level meditations in a more stable way. As the body (which includes both the physical musculature and one's subtle channels) loosens up, energy flows better and the mind loosens up and is freed of tension as well. The more relaxed the body and mind are, the easier it is to reconnect with our own healing potential and our basic uncontrived state of being. In this way, physical healing yoga practices need not be seen as separate from or supplementary to the ultimate goal or purpose of yoga, the reuniting with our original nature.

Nejang For Everyone: Yoga as Medicine and the Importance of Physical Health as a Part of Spiritual Practice

The Nejang practices described in this book are safe and simple enough for almost anyone to use. These exercises can be used in the context of everyday life, more or less often and in various combinations, as readers find convenient. Some people are surprised when they hear that as a Tibetan doctor I prescribe Tibetan *lüjong* yoga practices for my patients. They may have heard that Tibetan yoga practices are very advanced and very secret, meant only for elite, highly-trained Buddhist yogis and yoginis whose sole focus in life is ultimate spiritual realization. For this reason they may not understand how it is possible that I could teach something like Nejang more broadly or openly.

As mentioned, the physical and energetic procedures involved in *tsa loong trulkhor* practices are typically quite advanced and require initiation and long-term spiritual training under a guru. While all human beings have the innate potential to transform their body, energy, and mind, *tsa loong trulkhor* practices require a certain suppleness of the physical body and pliability and freshness of the subtle energies, things which humans tend to lose as they age.

The vital energies involved in these practices are also very powerful – they can be quite unfamiliar, difficult to grasp, and potentially destabilizing unless one is sufficiently prepared, focused and dedicated enough to deal with them. To really master these kinds of practices, traditionally one ideally began one's training by around the age of eight[8].

One also had to conduct this training in the context of closed retreat while adhering to strict rules and spiritual precepts. As such, it is true that these practices have typically been the preserve of either monastic or non-monastic yogic professionals. Monastics' ritual, administrative, and scholastic obligations on the one hand, and non-monastic individuals' family and work responsibilities on the other have often presented challenges for practitioners who wish to gain mastery in channels-and-winds practice. It takes a lot of time, energy, and dedication to become proficient in these disciplines and *tsa loong* training is not really something that can be done on-and-off or casually if one wants to achieve the best results. While it is true that for centuries Tibetan non-monastic householder yogis and yoginis (known as *ngakpa* and *ngakma* in Tibetan) have preserved yogic disciplines by integrating spiritual cultivation into their everyday domestic lives, retreat-based practice has still been very important even for these village-based, family *ngakpa* and *ngakma*.

The exercises of Nejang Yoga are connected with broader *tsa loong* practices, yet you do not have to be a professional yogi or yogini living for years and years in a retreat cave to practice and benefit from them. As preparatory *lüjong* practices, Nejang exercises do not involve complicated manipulations of the channels-and-winds. Yet

---

8. The condition of our subtle body between age eight to sixteen is said to be most conducive for training in *tsa loong trulkhor* yogic practices. While Tibetan yogis and yoginis do definitely begin *tsa loong trulkhor* training later in life, this period is considered the optimum time for engaging in yogic disciplines. See footnote 18 for more details.

despite being very simple they are also very powerful. The twenty four exercises of Nejang Yoga described in this book were originally compiled together in a small text by the great Tibetan monk-scholar and yogi Butön Rinchen Drup (1290-1364). This text, on which this book is based, is called *The Trulkhor of the Six-Limbed Yoga (Jorwa Yenlag Drugi Trulkhor,* སྦྱོར་བ་ཡན་ལག་དྲུག་གི་འཁྲུལ་འཁོར།). The 'Six-Limbed Yoga' refers to the special system of tantric yoga training found in the Kalachakra tantra, a very important collection of tantric Buddhist teachings which was introduced to Tibet from Kashmir in the eleventh century. The twenty four Nejang exercises are a form of preliminary body training that loosens up, balances and heals individuals' bodies, energies, and minds to prepare them for the more advanced yogic practices connected with the Kalachakra teachings.

Butön Rinchen Drup (left) (1290-1364)

In the colophon to his Nejang text Butön Rinchen Drup explains that previous lineages of these practices from India had been somewhat hidden and dispersed, that is, scattered across various sources. He explains that because of this, he took it upon himself to copy out these practices from different texts and condense them properly and thoroughly into a single manuscript, for the benefit of future generations of practitioners. It was Butön's view that these exercises were very profound methods for harmonizing the body and its energies to prevent obstacles in spiritual practice further down the line. In compiling his instructions, Butön made it very clear that they were intended to be used to help alleviate everyday medical problems. As he states in his colophon, he compiled these essential Nejang *lüjong* yogic exercises so that "the diseases of all beings without exception, caused by the disturbance of the elements, would be cured". Master Butön's intention in sharing these methods was thus to benefit beings, not only on a spiritual level but on the level of basic physical health as well.

Butön's Nejang work is a short and pithy text. It primarily describes how to perform each of the twenty four exercises and then offers a concise description of the energetic and physical health benefits associated with each practice[9]. In Chapter Three of this book which outlines the actual Nejang practice, I provide a translation of these various benefits. Although these benefits mostly deal with physical health rather than conditions connected with subtle tantric anatomy or 'Vajra Body', I refer to them in this book

---

9. In this book we offer both a fairly direct translation of Butön's instructions (listed in bold) and a more expanded translation, supplemented with oral commentary. This second translation provides a somewhat more precise and detailed explanation of how to perform each movement, and is based on direct oral instructions that I received from my own lineage-teachers when I received these practices in Tibet. Medical indications are then listed for each exercise following these two levels of translation.

as 'Tantric Benefits', since they derive from Butön's original text on tantric yoga. After listing the benefits of each exercise as recorded by Butön himself in his text, I then cite additional benefits or indications for each exercise, which are labelled as 'Medical Benefits'. These are benefits for each practice that have been observed and recorded by generations of doctors and yogic practitioners who have engaged in these exercises and have taught them to others. Over the centuries, Tibetan yogi-doctors who were familiar with Nejang exercises and who understood their value prescribed particular Nejang exercises for their non-initiated patients and less well-trained students, and a body of oral knowledge about the benefits of these practices emerged and developed. Many of the benefits listed in this book under the 'Medical Benefits' section are drawn from my own personal experiences of using Nejang exercises and suggesting them to students and patients over the past several years [10].

I have taught Nejang exercises to people of all ages and physical constitutions with positive results. These patients have been able to learn and implement Nejang practices despite having no prior yogic training. Nejang Yoga is a very gentle method for working directly with the body and its channels and subtle energies. As a doctor, I strongly believe that the cultivation of physical and mental health is as important for people on the spiritual path as for non-practitioners. I do not subscribe to the idea that because

---

10. While there is some overlap between the tantric and medical benefits listed, to fully understand the logic of some of the tantric benefits recorded by Butön a very deep study of the inner landscapes of our subtle anatomy and the teachings of the Kalachakra Tantra is required. The present chapter of this book offers a little more information on the Kalachakra system and a brief overview of the meaning of né ('points', 'places', 'power-spots' or 'abodes') in tantric Buddhism. For readers who would like to learn about the profound topic of the subtle or Vajra Body, Energy, and Mind, I will be publishing a more extensive book on this subject in the future.

one is a spiritual practitioner who renounces worldly attachments one should completely deny, ignore or dismiss these basic needs. A healthy body and a healthy mind are an important foundation for stable spiritual practice. While it is important to recognize that our mental and physical condition is as changeable and impermanent as all phenomena, it is a mistake to neglect our physical and mental wellbeing and treat it as inconsequential just because we are focused on seemingly loftier, less temporary, and less self-focused spiritual goals. Especially in these modern times, when sedentary lifestyles are the cause of so many different types of chronic diseases and depression has reached epidemic proportions around the world, physical yoga practices are extraordinarily beneficial.

I am thus very happy to share these Nejang techniques with readers. Like Master Butön, I pray that these methods will help heal innumerable diseases and health complaints. These simple but powerful exercises can benefit practitioners' minds and bodies on both a relative level, as well as assist practitioners seeking ultimate liberation.

Chapter 1: Energetic Body

Vajra Body, Energy, and Mind: Tsa - Loong - Thiglé

Energy Highways and Junctions: Channels and Chakras

Energy Flows: Subtle Winds

Karmic and Wisdom Winds

Mind's Essence and Energy's Richness

Nejang and the Sacred Abodes

Change Your Body, Change the World

24 Exercises: Gateways to the 24 Sacred Places

Inner Cultivation and the Conservation
of the Natural World

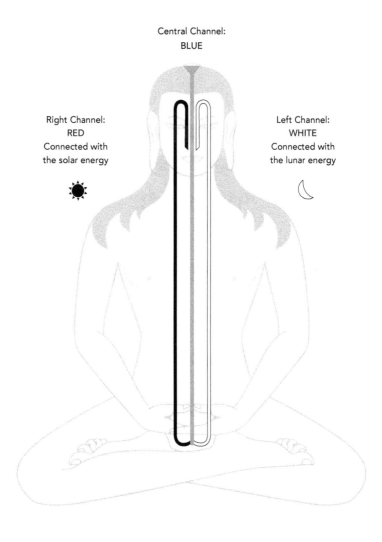

Central Channel:
BLUE

Right Channel:
RED
Connected with
the solar energy

Left Channel:
WHITE
Connected with
the lunar energy

Energetic Body

Vajra Body, Energy, and Mind: Tsa - Loong - Thiglé

According to tantric Buddhist teachings, our physical body as we know it, with its flesh and blood, bones, organs, and other material substances is only one aspect of our 'Body' in a wider sense. Similarly, our speech or voice that communicates with others is only one aspect of the broader dimension of 'Speech-energy', just as our everyday mind with all its thoughts, perceptions, and imaginations is only one aspect of our Mind. Beneath and within our ordinary Body, Energy, and Mind is a more subtle anatomy, what tantric texts call our Vajra Body, Vajra Speech or Energy, and Vajra Mind. This is our true nature, the subtlest aspect of our anatomy. The word 'vajra' (ᠪᠳᠠᠠ *dorje* in Tibetan) has many meanings but is most commonly translated as 'indestructible.' Vajrayana Buddhism (*dorje thekpa* in Tibetan) is the 'indestructible vehicle.' 'Indestructible' implies strength and power but more than that, it also points to non-duality. All the seemingly solid 'things' that we and other beings perceive lack any inherent, independent existence. They are compounded out of many parts and arise interdependently, through the coming together of various causes and conditions. All of these apparently stable and separate phenomena will eventually break down or decompose. Yet the basic nature of things, which Buddhists call 'emptiness' - emptiness of inherent, enduring self - can never be broken. It is indestructible, just like space itself. Many English speakers have the idea that emptiness implies a sort of void or nothingness. The truth is that rather than implying an absence or lack, emptiness is about latent possibility. Emptiness means that anything is possible, that there is always the space or potential for the manifestation of countless possibilities. This is the meaning of Vajra, and our own vajra nature is exactly like this.

Energy Highways and Junctions: Channels and Chakras

The three main components of our Vajra anatomy, each of which corresponds to Body, Energy, and Mind respectively, are *tsa* (རྩ་) or 'channels', *loong* (རླུང་), 'winds' or 'wind-energies', and *thiglé* (ཐིག་ལེ་), which is often translated as 'energy drop' or 'nucleus' (the Sanskrit names for these three components are nadi, vayu, and bindu). Our Vajra Body consists of a network of channels or pathways (*tsa*). Tantric texts describe three main 'queen' channels: the central channel (*uma*) and two lateral channels (*roma* and *kyangma*, the main right and left channels, respectively). The two side channels begin at the nostrils and travel down alongside the central channel, joining the central channel four finger-widths below the navel.

The right channel is associated with solar energy, while the left channel is associated with lunar energy. Although the right, solar channel is often represented as red and the left channel as white, the colors of these channels differ according to the specific text or lineage of teachings one is working with, and may be visualized differently as per instructions for the specific practice one is doing. Some texts state that the side channels are reversed in males and females. Notwithstanding this diversity, for the purposes of Nejang practice, we visualize the central channel as luminescent blue in color running from the crown of the head straight down to the genital area; the right channel as red; and the left channel as white, regardless of our sex and personal gender orientation.

Many people are familiar with the Sanskrit term Hatha Yoga, referring to Indian physical body, breath, and subtle energy-related yoga practices. In fact, the words 'ha' and 'tha' mean sun and moon and as we know, Yoga means to unite or join. Hatha Yoga is therefore

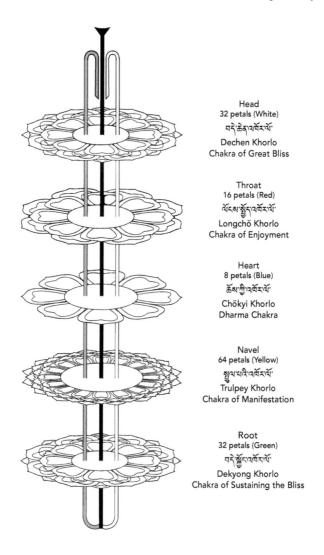

Head
32 petals (White)
བདེ་ཆེན་འཁོར་ལོ་
Dechen Khorlo
Chakra of Great Bliss

Throat
16 petals (Red)
ལོངས་སྤྱོད་འཁོར་ལོ་
Longchö Khorlo
Chakra of Enjoyment

Heart
8 petals (Blue)
ཆོས་ཀྱི་འཁོར་ལོ་
Chökyi Khorlo
Dharma Chakra

Navel
64 petals (Yellow)
སྤྲུལ་པའི་འཁོར་ལོ་
Trulpey Khorlo
Chakra of Manifestation

Root
32 petals (Green)
བདེ་སྐྱོང་འཁོར་ལོ་
Dekyong Khorlo
Chakra of Sustaining the Bliss

The five chakras

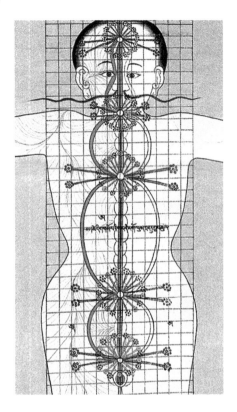

the union of sun and moon, or in Tibetan, *nyida kajor*. Through yogic exercises we are able to unite the seemingly polar solar and lunar energies represented by the right and the left channels. By doing so, we can harmonize the different poles of our nature, which empowers and balances our energy and life on a deep level.

Connected to each of these three main queen channels are 24,000 branch channels, which together create a vast and sophisticated network of interconnected pathways through which *loong* energy can flow. This is great news! The bad news is that these

72,000 channels unfortunately have the potential get 'knotted' in 84,000 ways too! These 84,000 'channel knots' (*tsa dü*), which correspond with the 84,000 mental afflictions referred to in Buddhist literature, can be loosened and released through physical yogic exercises, which, as explained in the previous chapter, can then have an impact on the mind.

When many channels crowd together they may form what is known in Tibetan as a *tsakhor*, or 'channel wheel', something more familiar to most English readers today under its Sanskrit title *chakra*. Chakras are dense nexuses of channels. Since many channels branch or radiate out from these nexuses, they are called chakras or 'wheels' and individual chakras are also sometimes said to have lotus-like 'petals'. While some people today treat chakras as separate from the channels, it is important to realize that the chakras of our subtle anatomy are traditionally included under the broader umbrella of *tsa*. Channels and channel-wheels are connected and work together in our bodies. The exact number and color of the chakras that one works with may differ from text to text and practice to practice. That said, Nejang and most other Tibetan yogic systems describe five main chakras, each located at different points along the central channel, namely: at the head, throat, heart center, navel, and genitals or root. The five chakras are positioned where the three main and other subsidiary channels join, creating condensed energy centers. Five is a very significant number in tantric Buddhism. It is connected with the five elements of earth, wind, fire, water, and space, which make up all of the phenomenal world and our physical and subtle bodies. The 84,000 mental afflictions mentioned above can be condensed down to the five principal Buddhist poisons of ignorance (or confusion), desire (or attachment), anger (or hatred), pride, and envy. These five poisons correlate with the five chakras, and can be released and transformed when the channel-wheels are unblocked and opened through yogic practice.

Energy Flows: Subtle Winds and Mental & Physical Well-Being

Our 72,000 channels serve as conduits for the flow of our *loong* energy. We can think of the relationship between our *tsa* and *loong* as being like the relationship of a car travelling on a road. Our *loong* energies are the cars and our *tsa* channels are the highways on and through which they travel. The nature of *loong* is to move and flow freely but when our channels are knotted or damaged *loong* gets stuck, just like how traffic cannot flow when roads are blocked, in disrepair, or overly congested. When *loong* gets congested or flows poorly it can stagnate and this in turn can result not only in physical health problems but mental and emotional issues as well. As noted, body-energy-and-mind are an interconnected continuum, a dynamic and integrated feedback system. The reason blocked energy affects our mind so strongly is because our *loong* is never in fact separated from our consciousness (*sem*), which in terms of the above analogy functions like the driver of our energy car. This driver-and-car pair, or what is known as *loong-sem* in Tibetan, circulates inside our channels. Our analogy can help us understand how the condition of our energy and channels can affect our mental and emotional wellbeing. When roads get blocked and traffic and congestion worsen, we know that drivers get stressed! So, in a similar way, the condition of our mind is affected by the state of our channels and winds.

This driver-and-car analogy is my own more modern update on an analogy that is used in traditional tantric texts to describe *loong-sem* or the union of energy and consciousness. These texts explain that the relationship between our energy and consciousness can be likened to a blind horse being guided by a legless rider. Here, our energy is the blind horse that runs wild and aimlessly, and our consciousness is the legless rider. Our consciousness can see and knows the path, it can direct the horse of our energy safely but crucially, it lacks any separate or alternative mode of transport of its own, apart from the vital energy of the *loong*. Thus, consciousness cannot get to its destination without the support of the horse's legs, or *loong's* capacity for motion. Moreover, the rider must control the wild horse with awareness and mindfulness so that she does not get dragged around aimlessly. One way to catch the horse so that it may be tamed, trained, and directed is through breath retention. While physical exercises are the best method for cleaning the channels, breath-work is the best method for cleaning and training the wind energy. Combining movement with breath retention as we do in Nejang Yoga or more advanced practices such as *tummo* is a powerful way to open our channels and to train the consciousness-energy duo in order to transform our body and energy into the Vajra Body and Energy of a Buddha[11].

Karmic and Wisdom Winds: The Yogic Transmutation of Energy

Our *loong* energy has two main components: the gross, or karmic wind (*lé loong*) and the subtle wind. Subtle wind-energy has both an impure and pure aspect, the second of which is described as 'wisdom', 'primordial wisdom' or 'gnostic' wind (*yeshe loong*). One of the primary functions of yogic practice is to transform the ordinary karmic or 'worldly' winds which run throughout the 72,000 branch channels into wisdom wind by drawing them into the central channel where our wisdom wind, the most pure and subtle form of our consciousness resides. *Bumpachen* 'the great vase' yogic exercise which will be taught in Chapter Three is one of the most effective procedures for transforming our karmic winds into wisdom winds. As will be explained, Vase breathing works by

---

11. The specific mechanisms of breath retention and how it affects our *loong* energy will be explained in detail in Chapter Three.

The Five Root Winds & Their Location in the Body		
Root Loong	Chakra	Location
Life-Sustaining Wind སྲོག་འཛིན་རླུང་ sogdzin loong	Head Chakra	Head, Throat, Chest
	• The principal wind, from which the other four are derived • Connects the body with the mind and energy • Controls functions such as swallowing, breathing, salivation, sneezing and hiccups • Provides clarity to the intellect and sensory perceptions and ensures the functioning of memory	
Ascending Wind གྱེན་རྒྱུ་རླུང་ gyengyu loong	Throat Chakra	Nose, Tongue, Throat
	• Controls the vocal expression • Generates physical and mental strength • Clears the complexion • Gives courage • Provides focus and willpower and makes the memory clear	
All-pervasive Wind ཁྱབ་བྱེད་རླུང་ khyapché loong	Heart Chakra	Heart, all parts of body, particularly the joints
	• Produces the heartbeat • Encourages the movement of the heart and body • Responsible for the bodily movements of walking • Opens and closes the doors of the senses and the skin pores	
Fire-accompanying Wind མེ་མཉམ་རླུང་ ményam loong	Navel Chakra	Stomach, Small Intestine, All internal organs
	• Presides over digestion and assimilation of food • Regenerates the body constituents	
Descending Wind ཐུར་སེལ་རླུང་ tursel loong	Root Chakra	Colon, Rectum, Large Intestine, Urinary Bladder, Genitals, Thighs
	• Regulates the retention and elimination of reproductive fluids (sperm and eggs), blood, feces and urine • Assists with delivery during childbirth	

'churning' karmic winds into the 'butter' of rarified wisdom wind. Likewise, retaining the breath as we do when performing the Nejang exercises is yet another method for drawing the karmic winds from inside the 72,000 branch channels into the central channel where they can then be transformed into wisdom winds.

Gross or karmic *loong* can be divided into five root and five branch *loongs*. Of these, the five root *loongs* are the most relevant for our purposes in this text. The five root *loongs* can be influenced through the basic meditative posture used in Nejang practice, i.e. The Seven Point Posture of Vairocana (see Chapter Three) and can be manipulated and affected in specific ways through the different Nejang exercises. The preceding chart describes the basic function of each of the root *loongs*, as well as their location in the body (both energetically in the chakras, and anatomically in the physical body)

Mind's Essence and Energy's Richness: 'Drops' or Thiglé

The third component of our Vajra Anatomy is *thiglé* or bindu in Sanskrit, the 'essential drops' which comprise the subtlest aspect of our mind. *Thiglé* is connected with our emotions, feelings, perceptions, and mood. A loose correlation can be made between *thiglé* and our hormones, although there are several levels and dimensions of *thiglé*, many of which surpass what current biomedical science can measure. Ultimately though, by working with *thiglé*, we transform our ordinary minds into non-dual bliss, which is the fully awakened mind of a Buddha – open, limitless, and joyful. The most direct method for transforming *thiglé* is Karmamudra or tantric sexual yoga practice. This is because when we work skillfully with our sexuality we engage directly with the energy of bliss in our body and mind. Even so, all forms of yoga and meditation work to some extent with our essential energy drops, since wherever there is mind, there is *thiglé*. Working with the breath is a powerful method for working with *thiglé*, because *thiglé* is directly related to our *yeshe loong*. When we increase our *yeshe loong* through breath retention and other aspects of yogic practice, we increase our *thiglé* in turn, thereby enhancing our capacity for realizing the blissful nature of mind.

The three aspects of *tsa, loong*, and *thiglé* can never be separated. Just as the channels depend on the physical body to exist, the *loong* depends upon the channels, and the *thiglé* depends on the *loong* energy. That is why basic posture is such an essential component of all yoga and meditation instruction. It is said that when the body is straightened, as in the seven point seated posture of Vairocana which is the basic Nejang posture, then the channels are straight as well; when the channels are straight then the *loong* energy flows freely; and when the *loong* energy flows freely, then the *thiglé* are balanced and the mind naturally comes to a state of blissful rest and ease. Thus, simply by aligning the physical body correctly we create the conditions for the mind to return to its pure, natural state. The connection between *tsa, loong*, and *thiglé* is captured in another traditional analogy, in which our channels are described as a house, the *loong* energy as the person living in the house, and the *thiglé* as the precious jewels or wealth that the person possesses and enjoys. Our vital energies are housed within the protective and supporting architecture of our channels and our *thiglé* are the most precious, valuable, and refined distillation of our energies, a treasure which ought to be protected and enjoyed. It is possible to increase our riches or to deplete them, to secure them or to take them for granted. The practice of yoga helps to maintain and renovate the structure of our home, the over-arching framework and foundation of our channels. This framework is crucial for living a stable and happy life, and provides a basic foundation for us to fully enjoy the richness of our being without obstacles.

Nejang and the Sacred Abodes: The Wheel of Time and Pilgrimage to Inner & Outer Dimensions

As mentioned in the Introduction, the twenty four Nejang Yoga exercises described in this book were originally collected together and written down by the great thirteenth century Buddhist master, Butön Rinchen Drup (བུ་སྟོན་རིན་ཆེན་གྲུབ། 1290-1364). Born to a family of adherents of the *Nyingma* or 'old' school of Tibetan tantric Buddhism, Butön Rinchen Drup was later ordained as a monk in the Sakya school. He went on to become the eleventh abbot of Zhalu Monastery in the Tsang province of Central Tibet at the age of thirty one, a position he held for thirty seven years. Considered to be an emanation of the historical Buddha himself, he was a great scholar, prolific writer, historian, artist, architect, astrologer, teacher, and

tantric yogi saint[12]. Most relevant for our purposes, he was also a prominent expert in and promoter of the Kalachakra Tantra.

A visual representation of the teachings and iconography of the Kalachakra Tantra.

---

12. A siddha in Sanskrit (*druptop* in Tibetan) meaning 'accomplished one' or 'one with spiritual accomplishments' referring to a practitioner of tantric yoga who has achieved profound realization and seemingly miraculous powers as a result of their pratices.

Kalachakra is a Sanskrit word meaning the 'wheel' or 'cycle' of 'time' (*du kyi khor lo* དུས་ཀྱི་འཁོར་ལོ). It refers to a specific collection of tantric Buddhist texts and teachings that were introduced to Tibet from Kashmir and translated into Tibetan in the eleventh century. As one of the last major Vajrayana scriptures to be transmitted to and popularized in Tibet from the Indian sub-continent, it contains many unique features and explanations not found in other tantric scriptures. Although the contents of the Kalachakra tantra are extremely diverse, covering everything from yoga to alchemy, astrology, embryology, and millennial prophecy, the principal teaching of the Kalachakra tradition is that the human body is a microcosm of the macrocosmic universe. Put differently, the entire universe is contained within our human form. As such, by mastering our individual body and its subtle energies, it is possible to gain mastery over time and the universe.

One important method for mastering time and space as outlined in the Kalachakra Tantra is the transformation of the physical and energy body through the practice of yoga. The Kalachakra Tantra outlines a distinctive six-limbed system of yoga as part of its instructions for *Dzogrim* or the 'Completion Stage' of tantric Buddhist yoga. In Vajrayana, Completion Stage meditation or yoga practices are the main way to work with and transform *tsa loong* and *thiglé*.

The six-fold system of *Dzogrim* practice found in the Kalachakra tantra (not to be confused with the Six Yogas of Naropa referenced in the Introduction) shares some terminology in common with the non-tantric Indian system of Ashtanga Yoga as described in the *Yoga Sutras* by Patanjali, composed around 400 C.E. The Ashtanga or 'eight-limbed' system is a complete and comprehensive system of yogic practice that begins with instructions on moral conduct and then progresses to teachings on the cultivation of meditative concentration and absorption. These days, while many people are familiar with Patanjali's Ashtanga yoga system[13], the Kalachakra's six-limbed yogic tradition is less well-known. The chart below offers a comparison of the six limbs of the Tibetan Kalachakra yoga system and the eight limbs of Patanjali's system. If one compares the Sanskrit names for the limbs in each system, their similarity becomes clear:

Kalachakra Yoga:
1. *so sor dud pa* སོ་སོར་སྡུད་པ།– Withdrawal (Sanskrit: pratyahara)
2. *sam ten* བསམ་གཏན།- Meditation (Sanskrit: dhyana)
3. *sog tsal* སྲོག་རྩོལ།- Wind/Breath control (Sanskrit: pranayama)
4. *dzin pa* འཛིན་པ།– Retention (Sanskrit: dharana)
5. *jé dren* རྗེས་དྲན།– Recollection (Sanskrit: anusmriti)
6. *ting ngé dzin* ཏིང་ངེ་འཛིན།– Absorption (Sanskrit: samadhi)

Astanga Yoga:
1. Yama: Moral Precepts
2. Niyama: Spiritual Disciplines and Observances
3. Asana: Physical Posture(s)
4. Pranayama: Breath Control
5. Pratyahara: (Sensory) Withdrawal
6. Dharana: Concentration
7. Dhyana: Meditation
8. Samadhi: Absorption

---

13. Although the Ashtanga system found in Patanjali's *Yoga Sutras* was a major inspiration for the more recent Ashtanga-Vinyasa Yoga practices that were developed in the twentieth century in Mysore, India, and which are now practiced all over the world, these modern practices are far from identical with Patanjali's own teachings.

Looking at this chart we can see that the last five of the eight limbs of Ashtanga Yoga are all included within the Kalachakra system. Although the first three limbs of the Ashtanga system (which stand as a sort of preparation for the main meditative practices that come after) are not included as formal categories in the Kalachakra's six-limb system, moral discipline and physical postures or asana are nonetheless a crucial component of all Tibetan tantric yoga practice.

Where the Kalachakra system diverges quite distinctly from Patanjali's is in the centrality of partnered sexual yoga practice for the application of its instructions on working with *tsa, loong,* and *thiglé*.[14] The first four limbs of the Kalachakra prepare the practitioner for the practice of *tummo* or inner heat yoga and Karmamudra, or heat-and-bliss yoga that involves practice with a physical (or visualized) sexual partner, which is the main focus of the fifth limb of the Kalachakra system called 'Rememberance'. Thus, while the correlations between Ashtanga and Kalachakra yoga systems are interesting and deserve further study, it is important to realize that the much later Kalachakra teachings are tantric in orientation, unlike Patanjali's. Although the classification schemes and some of the main meditative techniques used in these two systems may be similar, they ultimately differ in how they understand the goal of yoga. While Patanjali's system focuses on 'cessation' or restraint of mental elaborations and disturbances to experience the underlying nature, Tibetan tantric yoga emphasizes the total transformation of Body, Energy, and Mind into their enlightened Vajra forms.

---

14. Readers can find a fuller explanation of tantric orientations and Tibetan sexual yoga practices in my book *Karmamudra, the Yoga of Bliss: Sexuality in Tibetan Medicine and Buddhism* (Chenagtsang 2018).

Change Your Body, Change the World: Tibetan Prostration as a Form of Yoga

For people who are accustomed to thinking of yoga practices as primarily being about strengthening and toning the physical body, the idea that exercising one's physical body can transform both inner and outer worlds can be a little hard to grasp. One of the most common and famous everyday religious practices performed by Tibetans offers some useful insights into this possibility: the practice of prostration. Images of Tibetan pilgrims performing full-body prostrations for incredible distances along Tibet's beautiful and sacred landscapes are a favorite subject for photographers. These Tibetan pilgrims may spend years of their lives making pilgrimage by performing full-body prostrations along with each step or few steps they take, as they travel to and around sacred mountains and other holy sites. This process is said to accumulate great merit, combat pride and ego, and purify one's karma.

Prostration is a physical practice in which Tibetan Buddhists stretch their body flat on the ground as an act of reverence and devotion in the presence of holy beings and objects that are considered to be representations or embodiments of the Buddha's Body, Energy, and Mind. For this reason, many people think of prostration as primarily a devotional practice, as a special way to express deep reverence for outer sacred beings and forces. Yet while prostration is indeed a common expression of devotion for Buddhists, there is also a more inner, yogic dimension to prostration practice, as well as many health benefits. As a practice, full body prostration or *chaktsal* in Tibetan is often accompanied by special chanted prayers or liturgies. Like *lüjong trulkhor* exercises, it is also typically repeated many times in succession and is an excellent metaphor for the challenges of life, in which every time we fall down, we have the strength to stand up again. Medically, prostrations are excellent for the heart, respiratory system, blood circulation, and digestion. We can thus see that prostration practice involves directing and refining Body, Speech or Energy, and Mind in a thoroughly integrated way, just like with yogic practices.

The inner, yogic aspects of prostration are made explicit in a beautiful prayer often attributed to the founder of the Sakya lineage of Tibetan Buddhism (the same school into which Butön was ordained), a great master known as Sakya Pandita (1182-1251). Sakya Pandita is thought to have composed this prayer to remind practitioners of the deeper significance of prostration, and how it works on multiple levels as a form of spiritual cultivation. This prayer, which shows how each gesture or disposition cultivated as part of prostration is linked with key elements of Buddhist view, conduct, and motivation, is still used by practitioners in the Sakya lineage today:

༄༅། །ཕྱག་འཚལ་སྐབས་འདོན་རྒྱའི་སྐྱོན་ཚིག་ས་པཎ་གྱི་ གསུང་བཞུགས་སོ།།

བདག་གིས་མཆོག་གསུམ་དམ་པར་ཕྱག་འཚལ་བས། བདག་དང་འགྲོ་ ཀུན་སྡིག་སྒྲིབ་དག་པར་ཤོག།
ལག་གཉིས་མཉམ་པར་ཐལ་མོ་སྦྱར་བ་ཡིས། ཐབས་དང་ཤེས་རབ་ཟུང་འཇུག་ཐོབ་པར་ཤོག།
ཐལ་མོ་སྙིང་གའི་གཏུག་ཏུ་སྦྱར་བ་ཡིས། དོག་མིན་དགའ་ལྡན་གནས་སུ་བགྲོ་ དཔར་ཤོག།
ཐལ་མོ་སྙིང་མཚམས་དཔལ་བར་སྦྱར་བ་ཡིས། ལུས་ཀྱི་སྡིག་སྒྲིབ་ཐམས་ཅད་དག་པར་ཤོག།
ཐལ་མོ་མགྲིན་པའི་ཐད་དུ་སྦྱར་བ་ཡིས། དག་གི་སྡིག་སྒྲིབ་ཐམས་ཅད་དག་པར་ཤོག།
ཐལ་མོ་སྙིང་གའི་ཐད་དུ་སྦྱར་བ་ཡིས། ཡིད་ཀྱི་སྡིག་སྒྲིབ་ཐམས་ཅད་དག་པར་ཤོག།
ཐལ་མོ་སྦྱར་བ་སོ་སོར་ཕྱེ་བ་ཡིས། གཟུགས་སྐུ་གཉིས་ཀྱི་འགྲོ་ དོན་བྱེད་པར་ཤོག།
ཀེང་གཉིས་ཕུས་མོ་ས་ལ་བཙུགས་པ་ཡིས། བཅུ་གཅིག་ཀུན་ཏུ་འོད་ཀྱི་ས་ཐོབ་ཤོག།
ཡན་ལག་བཞི་པོ་བཀུག་བསྐུམས་བྱེད་པ་ཡིས། འཕྲིན་ལས་རྣམ་བཞི་ལྷུན་གྱི ས་གྲུབ་པར་ཤོག།
རྩ་རྒྱུས་ཐམས་ཅད་བཀྱངས་བསྐུམས་བྱས་པ་ཡིས། རྩ་མདུད་ཐམས་ཅད་མ་ལུས་གྲོ ལ་བར་ཤོག།
སྐྱལ་ཚིགས་དྲུག་མར་དགུ་དགུགས་བྱེད་པ་ཡིས། རྒྱུད་རྣམས་མ་ལུས་དྲུག་མར་ཆུད་པར་ཤོག།
ས་ལ་ཐུག་ནས་ཡར་ལ་ལྡང་བ་ཡིས། འཁོར་བར་མི་གནས་ཐར་ལམ་ཐོབ་པར་ཤོག།

དེ་ནས་ལན་མང་དུ་མར་ཕྱག་འཚལ་བས། ཞི་བར་མི་གནས་སེམས་ཅན་འདྲེན་པར་ཤོག།
བདག་སོགས་བརྒྱངས་ཕྱག་ཕྱལ་བའི་དགེ་བའི་མཐུས། གནས་སྐབས་ཚེ་རིང་ནད་མེད་ཕུན་ཚོགས་ཤོག།
འཆི་ཚེ་བདེ་བ་ཅན་དུ་སྐྱེས་ནས་ཀྱང་། རྟོགས་པའི་སངས་རྒྱས་གོ་འཕང་མྱུར་ཐོབ་ཤོག།
ཕ་མ་སེམས་ཅན་ཐམས་ཅད་བདེ་དང་ལྡན་གྱུར་ཅིག། ནན་འགྲོ་ཐམས་ཅད་ཧྲག་ཏུ་སྟོང་བ་དང་།
བྱང་ཆུབ་སེམས་པ་གང་ན་སུ་བཞུགས་པ། དེ་དག་ཀུན་གྱི་སྨོན་ལམ་འགྲུབ་གྱུར་ཅིག །ས་ཏ་མངྒ་ལཾ།།

"The aspiration prayer to be chanted when one performs prostrations as taught by Sakya Pandita.

By paying homage to the Three Sacred Jewels, may my own and all other beings' wrongdoings and obscurations be purified! Through placing my two hands together palm joined to palm may I obtain the indivisible union of means and wisdom! By placing my clasped palms to the crown of my head may I travel to Ogmin Ganden, the blissful, unsurpassed Pure Land! By touching my palms between my eyebrows at the forehead may all the sins and obscurations of my body be purified! By touching my palms to my throat may all the sins and obscurations of my speech be purified! By touching my palms to my heart-center may all the sins and obscurations of my mind be purified! Through separating my joined palms may the two form bodies – the Sambhogakhaya and Nirmanakaya – work on behalf of all beings! Through planting the knees of my two legs on the ground may I obtain the eleventh bhumi, the Buddha-stage of total luminosity! By stretching out and contracting my four limbs may I instantly and perfectly accomplish the four [tantric] activities! By stretching out and contracting all my tendons and [gross and subtle] channels may I release every channel-knot without exception! By bending my spine and central channel may all loong winds without exception enter into the central channel! By touching the ground and rising up again may I not remain in samsara and go on to achieve the Path of Liberation! Through then prostrating downwards again many more times may I not merely abide in peace but go on to lead sentient beings [out of samsara]!

Through the power of the merit of offering such fully extended, full-body prostrations for myself and others may I and they have abundant and long lives free from illness! Upon death may we be reborn in the Blissful Pure Land of Dewachen and swiftly obtain the perfected state of a Buddha!

May all mother-and-father sentient beings have happiness! May all the lower realms of negative rebirth be forever empty! Wherever Bodhisattvas might reside may all their prayers be accomplished! SARVAMANGALAM!"

In his prayer, Sakya Pandita explains how the physical actions involved in full-body prostration affect one's *loong* or inner energies. His mnemonic liturgy reminds the practitioner that her body and actions are a microcosm for all existence, a staging ground for the wellbeing and fate of all beings. Sakya Pandita makes it clear that the outer actions of prostration are linked to inner experiences and transformations. In this way, pilgrimage is not just about visiting external locations but about using our perception of outer locations and activities as a ground for purifying and transforming our awareness. It is for this reason that Sakya Pandita proclaims that when the practitioner touches their clasped palms to the crown of their head this creates the conditions for them to travel to the highest of blissful, 'pure lands'. Even though people might imagine Buddhist pure lands or realms of bliss and spiritual accomplishment as heavens or parallel dimensions located somewhere out there, real yogis and yoginis know that these pure realms are ultimately located within them, are states of being that point to their own potential.

The idea that our own human body and potential is the ultimate temple or holy site is central to Indian and Tibetan tantric yoga traditions. This concept was clearly expressed and celebrated by the Indian tantric Buddhist siddha or saint, Saraha, in one of his famous teaching songs. A version of one of Saraha's profound teaching songs as translated in the *Tengyur*, or Tibetan Buddhist collection of translated treatises, reads:

འདི་ནི་ཟླ་བ་རྒྱ་མཚོ་ཉིད་དང་ངོ། །འདི་ནི་གངྒཱའི་རྒྱ་མཚོ་ཉིད་དང་ངོ། །བཱ་རཱ་ཎསྲི་འས་ལ་སྲྭ་ལ་ཏི། །འདི་ནི་ཟླ་བ་གསལ་བྱེད་ཉིད། །ཞིང་ཀུན་གནས་དང་ཉེ་བའི་གནས་སོགས་པ། །ཕྱིན་ཏེ་བལྟས་པའི་རྟོགས་པ་གང་སྩུ་མ། །ལུས་དང་འདུ་བའི་སྲུ་གནས་གཞན་ན་མེད།།

"Right here [in this body] are the moon and ocean themselves, right here is the ocean of the Ganges itself, Varanasi and Srayaghayati, right here is the illuminating moon! I have been to all the [holy/pure] realms or locations, to the né and the pilgrimage sites surrounding them [i.e. nyerné], but whatever realization there is to speak of that may have come from seeing them, cannot compare with that [which comes from] the né of this body."
- Saraha, in the *Doha Dzökee Lu*

As an outward journey, pilgrimage is an important practice in many religious traditions. Such outer pilgrimage can function as a form of religious austerity or asceticism: by undertaking this arduous journey with resolve and the proper intention, one can purify one's karma through the hardships one encounters along the way, one can train one's mind and cultivate equanimity. Pilgrimage can also be seen as an act of devotion and a source of blessings and grace. Pilgrims travel to special locations so they can immerse themselves in the unique atmospheres of these holy places as a support for spiritual practice. They visit these sites so that they can 'meet', honor, and interact with the energies and beings that reside in those places. Since pilgrimage sites are often places were great adepts of the past stayed and achieved profound spiritual accomplishments, these places are like reservoirs of blessings which we in the present can tap into and benefit from.

Even so, while ordinary pilgrims may treat outer actions and holy sites as external realities to which they must submit themselves or pay homage in order to gain blessings, tantric yoga's non-dual approach acknowledges that inner and outer realities reflect and depend on each other. While Indian and Tibetan yoginis and yogis may still see great value in physically visiting holy places and pilgrimage sites, they remember that the ultimate point of yoga and meditation practice is inner transformation. With this view, outer realities support and merge with inner ones. Ultimately, when we discover the divine, pure, and blissful nature of our own Body, Energy, and Mind then the whole world is purified as well.

24 Exercises: Gateways to the 24 Sacred Places

Understanding the relationship between inner and outer transformation and locations allows us to gain a deeper appreciation of the twenty four exercises of Nejang Yoga and how these relate to the subtle anatomy. Nejang exercises are very simple to perform but also very profound. We can better grasp the deeper, spiritual significance of these exercises by reflecting on the meaning of this yoga's name, (*né jang*) which can be tranlsated as 'purifying the abodes' or 'locations'. On one level, the *né* or 'location' which we purify, refine, or cultivate in each Nejang exercise signifies a specific point or region in the body. As in healing therapies like massage, acupuncture, or moxibustion, here *né* implies special vital points on the body, which if manipulated can affect the flow of our energies and promote healing.

Yet *né* has other meanings as well. *Né* is the word used in Tibetan to describe one's 'home', a specific location for religious practice, and the special 'abode' of deities and sacred forces. When Tibetans say they are going on pilgrimage, they say that they are 'going to meet/see' or 'circle around the *né* or [sacred] abode'. In tantric yoga, when we engage with our *tsa, loong,* and *thiglé*, we begin to discover the sacred and divine within and as ourselves, within our own embodied experience. Tantric yogic practice is like an inner journey, a subtle, inner pilgrimage. Whatever powerful and transformative blessings or energies we can feel in an outer ceremony or in some feature of the outer landscape we are able to experience only because these energies are part of our own being as well. It is thus no coincidence that there are twenty four Nejang exercises. Each Nejang exercise corresponds to the so called 'twenty four sacred sites' or pilgrimage and practice places of tantric Buddhism. The twenty four sacred sites were originally developed in the context of Indian tantric Buddhism, and are listed in some of the most important Highest Yoga Tantra texts of the Tibetan Buddhist tradition. These sacred abodes were understood to correlate with inner energies, spiritual experiences, and subtle body yoga practices. At the same time, they were also physical locations spread across the Indian landscape. Tantric Buddhist yoginis and yogis would meet at these pilgrimage sites to practice inner tantric yoga practices and group rituals together. Certain special outer features of different pilgrimage sites in India were understood to correlate to aspects of the subtle anatomy and less visible, inner yogic processes. Because the Vajra body or 'body mandala' of the individual practitioner is ultimately equivalent or mirrored in the outer Vajra body or sacred mandala of the landscape, by visiting these sites and meeting and practicing with fellow initiates there, tantric Buddhist yoginis and yogis were able to support and empower their practices and fully realize the non-duality of outer and inner worlds.

When tantric Buddhist scriptures from India were transmitted to Tibet and translated, Tibetan masters began to associate the original twenty four sites in India with sacred locations and places of power more accessible to them in Tibet and the Himalayas. Because these masters understood that the twenty four *né* (or pitha in Sanskrit) were not just points on an ordinary map, it was entirely possible for them to discover equivalences of the twenty four Indian locations and the energies and processes they embodied closer to home. Visiting tantric power-spots and other great pilgrimage sites on this planet can have a powerful impact on our mind and practice, but as noted, tantric scriptures like the Kalachakra Tantra teach us that it also possible to visit these sacred lands using only the vehicle of our own physical body, the fuel of our energy, and the direction of our own consciousness. In the end, we don't have to travel anywhere at all, at least not in a conventional way.

For centuries, Tibetan scholars have argued about whether the sacred realms and locations mentioned in Indian and Tibetan sources ought to be understood as literal, outer locations, metaphors, inner, transcendent dimensions, or perhaps all of these at once. For example, Druptop Orgyenpa Rinchen Pal (1230 - 1309), the third Karmapa's guru, wrote of his journeys to the pure land of Oddiyana where he received teachings directly from the Dakini or female Buddha Vajravarahi. While many readers understood his account as a description of an actual pilgrimage to a geographical location on the map, many centuries later the great Tibetan scholar and yogi Gendün Chöphel (1903 - 1951) argued that Rinchen Pal's writings were not talking about an outer journey to a physical destination at all, but were rather a description of this master's profound inner journey to a pure dimension of experience that he was able to access through his own meditative awareness. Visiting these pure dimensions within our own body and mind is ultimately more powerful than visiting any physical place. This is the real meaning of Nejang Yoga.

Knowing about the names and features of the twenty four abodes is not essential for practicing or gaining benefits from Nejang practice. The purpose of this book is not to provide exhaustive explanations of these twenty four locations and their outer and inner significance and associations. Still, having a general understanding of these abodes can enrich our appreciation of Nejang Yoga and prevent us from being dismissive of its deceptively simple procedures. For readers who would like to learn more, the twenty four sacred places are discussed in both the Hevajra and Chakrasamvara Tantras. As I mentioned above, the majority of these abodes are linked to locations across the Indian sub-continent, Tibet, and the Himalayas. Still, it is important to realize that this list of sites is like an ideal or cosmic map or blueprint, one that can help us understand and deepen our relationship with zones of power and convergence all across the planet. Different locations in our planet's own Vajra Body or Mandala resonate and are connected with each other. So, although Mt. Kailash in the Himalayas appears to be a single mountain - one geographically fixed pilgrimage site on our planet - in reality it is energetically connected to many other mountains all over the world. I believe that Mt. Hood in the state of Oregon in the United States, for example, is one such 'other' Kailash. If one is perceptive enough, one can discern these connections. For this reason, these spots should not be thought of as isolated locations, but rather as power-points in our planet's own network of subtle channels and energies.

Inner Cultivation and the Conservation of the Natural World:

The correlation of the human body to the natural world reminds us of the important issue of environmental protection and preservation. The Kalachakra tantra teaches that outer and inner time, elements, and forces are all connected and reflect one another. Our individual bodies are composed of and are shaped by the same constituents and forces as the larger universe. The health of our individual bodies and the health of our planet are intimately related. If our outer environments are damaged or polluted, then beings can be affected on all sorts of levels, physically, mentally, and spiritually. Following the logic of the Kalachakra tantra and the general Buddhist principle of inter-dependent arising and causation, this mistreatment of the environment not only affects those living in and around these specific geographic areas but all beings everywhere. Conversely, by purifying our own bodies and channels through yoga, breath-work, mantra, and meditation, we can have a positive impact on the greater environment, on the subtle anatomy of the entire planet as well. While we don't always have control over the environment at large, we can always take responsibility for ourselves and our actions. We should not think of ourselves only as a continuum of the three gates of Body, Energy, and Mind, but actually as a continuum of Body, Energy, Mind, and Planet too. All four aspects are interconnected and must be cared for and nourished to promote total health. We have a responsibility and need to take care of our planet in the same way that we do our own physical bodies.

In Vajrayana literature, we find references to *nedak* who are the 'owners or masters of the abodes'. These spirit beings are protectors of the sacred places, special guardians who watch over these lands to ensure their preservation. This is part of the reason why it is often said that power-spots and important pilgrimage sites are extremely difficult to access for ordinary people. These spaces are protected not only by rough terrain but also potentially wrathful spirits who may create obstacles for those who try to enter with impure motivation. In Jigme Lingpa's famous feast offering song, for example, there is a line that invokes these protectors of the twenty four sacred places. These spirit protectors or land-lords are invited to come and partake of the blessed ritual offerings which are made available during tantric celebrations, along with all the Buddhas, Bodhisattvas, and other tantric deities and realized masters. Making offerings, real or imagined, is one very common Buddhist technique for pacifying and supporting the forces connected with our natural world, for removing obstacles, and for restoring balance in a world constantly plagued by negative, disruptive influences. Today, His Holiness the fourteenth Dalai Lama regularly conducts elaborate, large-scale initiation ceremonies for the Kalachakra tantra cycle in different locations all over the world. The rites associated with these initiations help placate, subjugate, and balance spiritual forces and to create the energetic conditions for peace, healing, and harmony on a global scale. Accordingly, these ritual events are today referred to as 'Kalachakra for world peace' in English, and have been performed more than thirty times over the last sixty years for gatherings of tens of thousands of people. As a practitioner of tantric yoga, the Dalai Lama understands the importance of coordinating inner and outer activities to protect our sacred environment and to preserve harmony in the world. His dedication in undertaking these mass rituals in various locations along with his promotion of more material, outer environmental activism, makes clear his commitment to such matters, and his appreciation of the principle of interdependence.

It is clear then that the *né* or 'locations' involved in Nejang Yoga can be understood on many different levels. More than just specific areas of the body, these *né* that are activated and purified through Nejang Yoga point to how we can access profound dimensions of being by untying the knots within our own subtle anatomy. When we practice the exercises of Nejang Yoga it is useful to keep this greater view in mind so that we do not think that just because these exercises are simple or easy to do, they are somehow ordinary or mundane. The power and effectiveness of this form of yoga does not just depend on how capable we are at performing specific, physical movements or technical procedures. It also depends on our outlook, and our capacity and willingness to tune in to more internal dimensions of being. If we have good understanding and motivation, and practice with focus and awareness, we can make great gains through even the simplest of practices. As one of my favorite quotations goes, a line often attributed to Leonardo Da Vinci, "simplicity is the greatest form of sophistication".

A more detailed look at the twenty four sacred abodes can be found in the appendices at the end of this book.

Chapter 2: Health Benefits of Nejang

Methods of Treatment in Tibetan Medicine

Health Benefits of Yoga & Tibetan Longevity Techniques

The Sense Organs: Flowers of our Inner Organs

Happy Body, Happy Mind: Health is Wealth

Spiritual Healing & Holistic Health

Diet   Lifestyle   Medication   External Therapies   (Spiritual Healing)

གསོ་བྱེད་ཐབས།

Tree of Treatment:
*The four methods of treatment taught in the Gyüzhi
(Four Medical Tantras) and the additional method
of 'spiritual healing'. For a more detailed explanation
of the theory and practice of Tibetan Medicine, please refer
to the book, The Tibetan Book of Health: Sowa Rigpa,
the Science of Healing (Chenagtsang 2017)*

Health Benefits of Nejang

Methods of Treatment in Tibetan Medicine

Sowa Rigpa (གསོ་བ་རིག་པ།), the Himalayan 'Science of Healing,' identifies two principal goals in the practice of medicine: to prevent imbalance and to cure disease. *Sowa* literally means 'to nourish,' but in a medical context it more specifically means 'to heal.' *Rigpa* has various meanings depending on the context, and can refer both to scientific 'knowledge' as well as to our innate primordial awareness. A more spiritual translation of *Sowa Rigpa* is the 'nourishment of awareness.' These nuanced layers of meaning are fitting for a sophisticated medical science that not only aims to bring balance to our physical health, but also to our mind and energy, all the while supporting our spiritual development.

The *Four Medical Tantras* (རྒྱུད་བཞི། *Gyüzhi* in Tibetan), the root texts of *Sowa Rigpa*, describe four principal methods of healing utilized in the Tibetan Medical tradition, which are conceived as branches of a single metaphorical healing tree. These four modalities used for healing are:

1) Diet - Specified per an individual's constitutional typology, circumstantial needs, season, age, environment, and numerous other factors.

2) Lifestyle - Including exercise, daily conduct, seasonal behavior, social habits, sleep, sexual health, and so on.

3) Herbal Medicine - Traditionally formulated from herbs, minerals, and other natural ingredients, and administered by a qualified *Sowa Rigpa* practitioner.

4) External Therapies - Including *Kunyé* oil massage, moxibustion, acupuncture, hot and cold compresses, bathing therapy, etc.

The first two branches are primarily concerned with *Sowa Rigpa*'s first aim of prevention, while the third and fourth branches are more concerned with the treatment of disease once it has already manifested. Of course, there is some overlap because gentle herbal medicine and external therapies can also be excellent preventative methods, and diet and behavioral changes are often essential in treating both chronic and acute conditions. According to this fourfold categorization, Nejang Yoga would fall into the second method of treatment, lifestyle. 'Lifestyle,' according to the *Four Medical Tantras*, is a broad and complicated topic, covering exercise, sleep, seasonal routines, social behavior, sexuality, and more. A healthy lifestyle is much more than just eating well and getting some exercise - it encompasses all aspects of one's life including our personal, communal, and spiritual life. Unlike modern medicine which often de-emphasizes the importance of lifestyle choices in favor of pharmaceutical prescriptions, surgical operations, and other aggressive treatments, Tibetan and other traditional medical systems have always viewed lifestyle as an essential aspect of maintaining health and balance. If we can keep ourselves healthy with a balanced diet and lifestyle, then we can hopefully avoid having to turn to extreme medical interventions down the line when it may already be too late for these to be entirely succesful.

Health Benefits of Nejang & Tibetan Longevity Techniques

The health benefits of Nejang derive from a few of its rather unique qualities. According to Tibetan Medicine, the breath is directly linked to the function of our mind. As explained in the previous chapter, respiration is one of the grosser aspects of our body's motility factor, known as *loong* or the 'wind' energy within the body. As we learned in the previous chapter, *loong* energy flows through the various channels (*tsa*) within the body, like a car on a highway. The mind is like the driver within that car, speeding down the road via the motility of the wind energy. When our wind energy becomes disturbed, our mental state can also become disturbed. But it doesn't stop there - *loong* imbalance can affect all systems of the body, causing metabolic disturbances, neurological pain, tachycardia, insomnia, and much more.

But just as imbalanced wind energy can cause disease, balanced *loong* can be an indispensable ally in preventing and treating illness on all levels. Both Tibetan medicine and tantric Buddhism talk about the ten *loong* energies (the five root winds and five branch winds) as being the power sources for our physiological

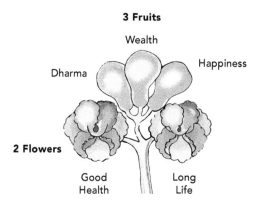

The two 'flowers' of good health and long life: the two results of a system brought into balance through Sowa Rigpa. From these flowers, the fruitional benefits of a balanced mind and body develop, known as the three 'fruits': dharma (spirituality and acceptance of the way things are), wealth (satisfaction and a sense of abundance), and happiness.

and spiritual potency and each has the basic capacity to support about ten years of life, if nothing is done to maximize their potential. If for each decade we have one *loong* energy battery which gets used up as the years pass, this means that the *average* human life span should be one hundred years. By slowing and extending the gap between the inhale and exhale with breath retention and practicing other rejuvenating techniques, we can recharge these batteries and extend our life even beyond one hundred years. Conversely, extreme sports can shorten our lifespan by causing us to breathe faster, with greater exhale.[15]

Breath control also has a profound effect on our mind and brainwave function. In studies conducted on practitioners of yogic breath retention, it has been shown that halting or slowing respiration allows more sustained and undisturbed experiences of deep meditation to arise. In one such study on subjects with no history of pranayama or yogic breathing practice, just three months of retained or slowed breathing exercises resulted in significant stimulation of the parasympathetic nervous system (the "rest and digest" system), with simultaneous suppression of sympathetic nervous activity (the "fight or flight" system)[16]. This supports the centuries of direct, contemplative research conducted in India and the Himalayas by masters such as Butön Rinchen Drup.

The specific health benefits of each of the twenty four exercises will be explained in more detail in Chapter Four, but one of the most simple and essential general benefits of Nejang is its power to counteract the deleterious effects of a sedentary lifestyle, a major

---

15. My forthcoming book, *The Tibetan Art of Rejuvenation* (*chulen*, literally "extracting the essence") will provide an in-depth description of the multitude of rejuvenation and anti-aging techniques taught from the perspective of both medical and yogic traditions.

---

16. Pal, Velkumary, and Madanmohan (2004). See Bibliography.

contributing factor to modern chronic diseases. Due to modern biomedical advances and widespread education about hygiene, great strides have been made in preventing the many acute illnesses and contagious epidemic diseases that killed countless people in the past. Today, these illnesses are no longer the primary threat to our wellbeing in most developed parts of the world. But while vaccines, antibiotics, and other Western medical treatments have saved many lives, a sedentary lifestyle and the burden of stress have become our killers, and chronic illnesses such as diabetes have become new, modern global epidemics.

The simple movements and self-massage of the Nejang practice warm and open the channels, which increases the flow of both energy and blood, resulting in many health benefits. The main causes of premature aging today are inflammation in the body, lack of oxygen, accumulation of toxins, and too much tension and stress in the body and mind. Stimulating the circulation of both blood and energy especially in conjunction with breath retention, can address all of these factors. By reducing inflammation, increasing levels of oxygen, releasing toxins, and relaxing the body and mind, Nejang Yoga works as a powerful rejuvenation practice.

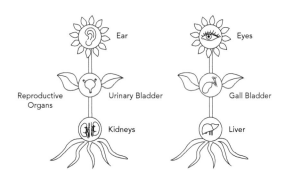

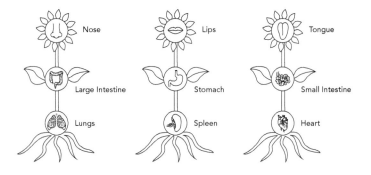

The Sense Organs: Flowers of our Inner Organs

In Tibetan Medicine (as well as Traditional Chinese Medicine), a correlation is drawn between the outer organs of the senses (ears, eyes, nose, tongue, and lips) and the inner organs. In *Sowa Rigpa*, the sense organs are depicted as five flowers which are connected to the roots of the flower (representing the five solid organs of kidneys, liver, lung, heart and spleen) via the stem (representing the five hollow organs of urinary bladder, gallbladder, large intestine, small intestine and stomach). We know that if the roots of a plant are sick or if the stem is damaged, the flower will also wither, so by simply looking at a flower we can assess the deeper health of the plant, even the condition of its roots, which are hidden underground. We can know if the plant is lacking in nourishment, water or light. It is exactly the same with the body - if the inner organs (solid or hollow) are not healthy, this will likely manifest symptomatically in the sense organs or their faculties, some examples being dryness or irritation of the eyes, tinnitus, or chapped or dry lips. Part of the Tibetan physician's diagnostic process involves observing the sense organs as well asking the patient questions about them in order to learn more about the state of the inner organs.

In Nejang Yoga, we can actually exercise or massage the sense organs in order to influence our inner organs. We cannot massage our kidneys directly but we can certainly massage our ears, which is a simple and practical way to indirectly affect both the kidneys, the bladder and reproductive organs, through the interconnection of the three parts of the 'plant' (flower, stem, and root). Likewise, rotating the eyes can influence the liver and gallbladder (as well as the eyes themselves), stretching the tongue affects the heart and small intestine and so on. These exercises can be done at any time of the day by taking a five minute break from work at your desk or even in your bed, making this practice an extremely convenient method for maintaining overall health. Elderly people who may lack strength and mobility in the body can still feel empowered to benefit themselves through these very easy-to-do exercises.

Both Traditional Tibetan and Chinese Medicine not only see a connection between the sense and inner organs but posit a connection between these organs and particular emotions as well. The kidneys are traditionally associated with fear, the liver with anger, the lungs with sadness or grief, the heart with anxiety and the spleen with confusion and anger. This means that by working with the sense organs through Nejang Yoga, we can influence not only our inner organs, but also their correlated emotions as well.

Happy Body, Happy Mind: Health is Wealth

A healthy lifestyle not only promotes good physical health - it also reduces stress and contributes to a happy and relaxed mind. If our mind is relaxed, then our physical health will naturally improve. 'Happiness' itself is considered to be one of the most important benefits of adhering to a *Sowa Rigpa* lifestyle. The study of human happiness has long been a very real topic in Tibet, not only spiritually, but also medically, as I believe it should be. Though not a literal translation, I often define *Sowa Rigpa* as 'The Science of Health and Happiness,' a more accurate and nuanced description of this ancient field of knowledge. Nejang Yoga and yogas in general are very powerful mood regulators. When the energy channels are blocked we experience not only pain in the physical body, but also low and unstable moods. Though *thiglé* (energy drops) discussed in the chapter on subtle anatomy is a vast and complex topic, I really believe that on some level, these *thiglé* can be correlated with "happy hormones" such as dopamine and seratonin. When the channels (*tsa*) are opened through yoga practice and the energy (*loong*) is able to flow freely, then these happy hormones can spread throughout the body, enhancing our mood. Retaining the breath has a similar effect of releasing these happy hormones resulting in a stable and long lasting sense of happiness and contentment. As we have seen, it is possible through both medical and spiritual techniques to extend one's life. However, equally important to the quantity of years one can live is the quality of life that we experience during those years. Living long is of little value if one does not also experience the joy of living.

Along with happiness, the two other fruits' of *Sowa Rigpa* discussed in the *Gyüzhi* (or the *Four Medical Tantras* that form the central textbook of Tibetan Traditional Medicine) are dharma (the experience of the truth of phenomena) and wealth (or material resources). Depending on our own spiritual orientation, dharma can refer to a sense of spiritual fulfilment as well as a meaningful integration with our true nature. If we are out of step with the way things are, then our suffering will increase. By bringing our mind, body, and energy into balance, we can more easily accept things the way they truly are. 'Wealth' can be interpreted as a sense of deep satisfaction and abundance, which isn't dependent on external circumstances. Many people have abundant material resources but still feel discontent and impoverished, this is especially true for those that are struggling with their physical and mental health. Contrarily, there are many people in this world who live in extreme states of poverty but still hold a strong sense of inner richness and contentment. Whether you are a spiritual seeker or one who is pursuing material comforts in life, the real motivation driving all humans is the simple wish to be happy and fulfilled. This is the true wealth, but without health unless you are a very highly accomplished meditator with deep spiritual realization, it is very difficult to experience that basic inner satisfaction and happiness.

Spiritual Healing and Holistic Health

In addition to its role as a form of exercise or therapeutic behavior, we can also place Nejang in an extra fifth category of treatment methods: spiritual healing. This modality is not conventionally included in the fourfold division of the *Four Medical Tantras*, but it is an essential aspect of healing discussed in many traditional texts. 'Spiritual healing' refers to a wide variety of techniques for healing the Body, Energy/Speech, and Mind. Physical yoga exercises and prostrations are examples of body healing practices that work with our channels; mantra recitation and breathing exercises work with our *loong* energy to bring balance to our speech and subtle energies; and meditation (of which there are many types) is the principal spiritual healing method for transforming the mind, which is connected with our *thiglé*.

Nejang is a single and complete practice that unifies all three aspects of Body, Energy, and Mind through the combination of physical yogic exercises, breath retention, and meditative concentration. As such it is a very complete and holistic practice, and one of the simplest methods for bringing spiritual healing to all aspects of one's being, including our physical and mental health. The most effective way to practice Nejang is by doing the exercises with strong awareness of the breath and focused mental concentration. Simply moving through the exercises as a physical routine will result in some physical benefits such as increased flexibility and improved blood circulation, but these benefits will be limited compared to the benefits that can come from treating the practice as a complete yoga of body, energy, and mind.

Chapter 3: The Preliminaries

Setting the Proper Intention: The Four Immeasurables

7-Point Posture of Vairocana

The Monk and the Monkeys

Ninefold Purification Breathing

Empty Body and Empty Channels Meditation

Vajra Chanting

Nejang Breathing: Partial Vase Breathing

Combining Nejang Exercises with Yogic Breath Retention

Contraindications for Breath Retention

Bumpachen

Contraindications for Bumpachen

Bumpachen and Astrology

སེམས་ཅན་ཐམས་ཅད་བདེ་བ་དང་བདེ་བའི་རྒྱུ་དང་ལྡན་པར་གྱུར་ཅིག །

**SEM CHEN TAM CHE DE WA DANG DE WE GYU
DANG DEN PAR GYUR CHIK**

May all beings have happiness and the causes of happiness,

སེམས་ཅན་ཐམས་ཅད་སྡུག་བསྔལ་དང་སྡུག་བསྔལ་གྱི་རྒྱུ་དང་བྲལ་བར་གྱུར་ཅིག །

**SEM CHEN TAM CHE DUK NGEL DANG DUK NGEL GYI
GYU DANG DREL WAR GYUR CHIK**

May all beings be free from suffering
and the causes of suffering,

སེམས་ཅན་ཐམས་ཅད་སྡུག་བསྔལ་མེད་པའི་བདེ་བ་དང་མི་བྲལ་བར་གྱུར་ཅིག །

**SEM CHEN TAM CHE DUK NGEL ME BE DE WA DANG
MI DREL WAR GYUR CHIK**

May all beings never be separated from the supreme joy
that is beyond all suffering,

སེམས་ཅན་ཐམས་ཅད་ཉེ་རིང་ཆགས་སྡང་གཉིས་དང་བྲལ་བའི་བཏང་སྙོམས་ལ་
གནས་པར་གྱུར་ཅིག །

**SEM CHEN TAM CHE NYE RING CHAK DANG NYI DANG
DREL WE TANG NYOM LA NE PAR GYUR CHIK**

May all beings abide in equanimity, free from attachment or
aversion to those near and far.

The Preliminaries

Setting the Proper Intention: The Four Immeasurables

Doing physical yogic practices such as Nejang can improve your health, happiness, and quality of life. But in the context of Buddhist practice, any meditation or yoga practice should be placed in the broader framework of seeking enlightenment for the benefit of all sentient beings. This means that whatever practice one does, it should be done with an altruistic motivation and sealed by dedicating the merit of one's efforts for the benefit of all.

Practicing Nejang with the intention to not only improve one's health and quality of life or to reduce pain but also with the authentic wish to be of benefit to others increases the potency of these simple exercises. Shifting the focus away from oneself and one's personal problems and adopting this larger perspective is not only beneficial for others but also for oneself. As a doctor I have seen that sometimes when a patient is overly focused on their own healing, their symptoms can actually be exacerbated. When they practice foundational Buddhist practices such as cultivating love and compassion for others as in the 'Four Immeasurable' practice that will be described here, they notice that their pain is reduced and they feel better.

Before beginning the practice, take a few moments to sit in a relaxed meditative posture and cultivate a feeling of love in your heart. One of the most classic Buddhist prayers used for this purpose is this prayer, known as the prayer of the 'Four Immeasurables' or *tsemay shee* in Tibetan. Each line of this prayer helps us to cultivate one of four immeasurable qualities associated with our Buddha-nature: immeasurable loving-kindness towards all beings equally, the wish for all beings to have happiness; immeasurable, unconditional compassion for all who suffer; immeasurable rejoicing in others' joy; and limitless, immeasurable equanimity or impartiality to all beings:

May all beings have happiness and the causes of happiness.
May all beings be free from suffering and the causes of suffering.
May all beings never be separated from the supreme
joy that is beyond all suffering.
May all beings abide in equanimity,
free from attachment or aversion to those near or far
(i.e attachment to loved ones and aversion for enemies)

Rather than reciting this prayer in a habitual or speedy way, take the time to contemplate its deep meaning and recognize the suffering that permeates all levels of this conditioned existence. Make a wish from the depths of your heart that all beings may be free of their pain. Start by extending this prayer towards someone that you naturally feel a sense of unconditional love for such as your mother or your child. Once you can genuinely feel this deep sense of love in your heart, try to extend this same feeling towards others that you may not have any particular feelings of kindness or aversion towards. See if you can hold them in your heart in the same way that you can so naturally hold your child or other loved ones in your heart. Then slowly think of those who disturb you in your life, those you might be jealous of and even those who have harmed you, and wish for them all to be happy and free of suffering too. If this is too difficult or if you have had traumatic experiences in your life that get triggered by this type of meditation, do not force yourself to do this last step at the beginning. Focus instead on strengthening and growing the love that you have in your heart for those that are close to you. As you give that love, you in turn receive it back in an unbroken cycle of giving and receiving.

According to Buddhist philosophy, since beginningless time we have have been wandering through samsara, the cycle of existence brought on by our ignorance and characterized by different types suffering. Samsara is comprised of six realms of existence: the upper realms of gods, demi-gods, and humans; and the lower realms of animals, hungry ghosts, and hell-beings. Eventually, with sustained practice of the 'Four Immeasurable' contemplations, we can begin to see all beings — our greatest love or worst enemy, the tiniest creature and even the beings throughout the six realms that we cannot see directly — as equals. This experience comes not from a contrived sense of love and compassion, but from the critical intelligence that understands that we have all actually been related to each other in countless different ways as we have cycled through samsara for aeons. It is only our current temporary conditions that cause us to have attraction or aversion for certain beings in this particular lifetime or moment. What equalizes us all is the identical Buddha nature that exists and is the same within every single sentient being, regardless of their conditions or their behavior. This view is the foundation of the Buddhist path.

"His Holiness the Dalai Lama refers to the
(9-fold Purification) breathing as the 'tranquilizer'
as it is extremely calming to the nervous system."

The Seven Point Posture of Vairocana

The basic posture from which we begin all of the Nejang exercises (except exercise number twenty four which can be done standing) is called the Seven Point Posture of Vairocana རྣམ་སྣང་ཆོས་བདུན། *(nam nang chö dün)*. The seven points of this posture position the body and channels in a way in which the five root *loong* energies are naturally balanced and are able to flow. As we have seen already, when the wind energies flow freely, the *thiglé* connected with the subtlest part of our mind will naturally become balanced and we can experience relaxation and happiness. Correct posture is therefore extemely important and can make our meditation feel less strenuous and strained.

The seven points of the posture are as follows:

If it is not comfortable to sit on the floor, the Seven Point Posture of Vairocana can be practiced while sitting on a chair with the spine straight and the two feet slightly apart and planted on the ground or with the ankles loosely crossed.

1. Sit cross-legged, ideally in the full lotus position. If this is not possible, sit in the half lotus position, in a more relaxed cross-legged position, or in the three-point posture with the two feet planted slightly apart on the ground and the arms clasping the upright knees.

   [**Balances the descending wind** (*tursel loong* ཐུར་སེལ་རླུང་།)]

2. Keep the spine straight, like a stack of golden coins.

   [**Balances the fire-accompanying wind** (*ményam loong* མེ་མཉམ་རླུང་།)]

3. Clasp the hands in vajra fists, with the thumbs pressing against the root of the ring fingers, and the other fingers wrapping around the thumb (the index fingers can remain extended).
   Press the back of the fists firmly into both groins.

   [**Balances the descending wind** (*tursel loong* ཐུར་སེལ་རླུང་།)]

4. Touch the tongue to the roof of the mouth, just behind the upper teeth. Leave the mouth slightly open - the teeth should not touch. Breathe freely through the nose and mouth.

   [**Balances the life-sustaining wind** (*sogdzin loong* སྲོག་འཛིན་རླུང་།)]

5. Straighten the arms and lift the shoulders, like folded eagle's wings.

   [**Balances the all-pervasive wind** (*khyabché loong* ཁྱབ་བྱེད་རླུང་།)]

6. Tuck the chin in slightly, like a swan.

   [**Balances the ascending wind** (*gyengyu loong* གྱེན་རྒྱུ་རླུང་།)]

7. Gaze at the tip of the nose or into the space just in front of the nose.

   [**Balances the life-sustaining wind** (*sogdzin loong* སྲོག་འཛིན་རླུང་།)]

The Monk and the Monkeys:

There is a funny story about this sevenfold posture of Vairocana that helps to illustrate its potency. In Buddhist teachings, we sometimes hear the term 'monkey mind' used to describe our busy minds that cannot rest, are always distracted, and jumping to and fro. This story says that once there was a monk meditating in an insolated cave high up in the mountains. A monkey walked by and spotted this monk sitting perfectly still in the seven point posture of Vairocana. Imitating this monk, the monkey also bound up his legs in the lotus position, raised his shoulders, straightened his arms, and opened his chest. What happened in this moment of adopting this posture was that his monkey mind suddenly ceased to run everywhere and he sat perfectly still and calm, with no wish to move. Soon other monkeys came by and seeing the monk and monkey sitting like that on the mountain, they also imitated their posture and were instantly brought into a state of meditative calm. The mountain was covered by perfectly still monkeys.

The point of this story is to show the power of the body to affect the mind. Normally we think we need to calm the mind by the power of the mind alone, but as we know from experience this can be very challenging. Our monkey minds do not want to stop running, no matter how much we tell them to. But if we simply sit up straight in this sevenfold posture, our physical body is aligned in a way that automatically causes our five *loong* energies to flow and become balanced, and when our energies flow freely, our mind naturally calms down without having to exert much effort. For example, by lifting the shoulders, our mind becomes more alert and by keeping the chin slightly down, the flow of the blood to the brain is slowed down which in turn calms the mind. The vajra fist position in which we block the root of our fourth fingers is a special protective hand position that both secures the vital energy inside the body and prevents negative influences from the outside from entering into the channels which originate at the tip of our fourth fingers. Each point of this posture has a very specific physiological effect that can be directly felt in the mind and body.

When the mind cannot rest, it can be very useful to direct more attention to the physical body and its movements, and to use the body as a gateway to meditation. This is the foundation of Nejang practice. Most Buddhist meditators know about and practice this basic posture, but they may not understand the connection between physical posture and *loong* energy and the natural effect that it has on the mind.

Preliminary Breathwork:
Ninefold Purification Breathing

Before beginning the Nejang exerices, it is beneficial to practice the ninefold purification breathing, otherwise known as 'the ninefold clearing out of dead air' རླུང་རོ་དགུ་ཕྲུགས་བསལ་བ། (*loong ro gu truk sel wa*). This breathing cleans out any toxicities or energy blockages held within the three main ('queen') channels and opens the nasal passage to promote free flow of breath. It is a simple and powerful practice that can be done first thing in the morning to balance the energies before starting the day, before bed to help improve the quality of sleep, or at any moment that one is feeling anxious or nervous. His Holiness the Dalai Lama refers to this breathing as the 'tranquilizer' as it is extremely calming to the nervous system. It is a powerful technique that both calms and cleanses the mind and energies.

In Buddhist philosophy it is said that the root cause of suffering is the 'three mental poisons' of desire (or attachment), confusion (or ignorance), and anger (or hatred). On a more physical level, these poisons can manifest in the body as the three *nyepas* (literally the three 'faults' but more commonly translated as the three humors) of wind (*loong*), phlegm (*beken*) and bile (*treepa*). In Ayurvedic medicine, these correlate to Vatta, Pitta, and Kapha. These dynamic energies are an expression of the five elements that make up one's physical, energetic, and mental body which when out of balance lead to various kinds of health problems. The heaviness of the earth and water elements combine to create the phlegm humor (*beken*) which is associated with confusion and lethargy; the heat of the fire element manifests as the bile humor (*treepa*) which can express itself as hot anger or agression; and the mobility of the wind element manifests as the wind humor (*loong*) which can manifest as attachments and desire, a sense of dissatisfaction that needs to be constantly stimulated. The space element is the backdrop of the four other elements, and present within each of the three humors.

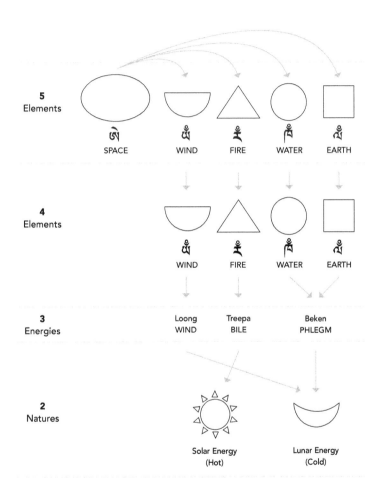

Constitutionally we are all born with a particular makeup of these three *nyepas*, derived from a combination of our mother and father's genetics as well as our personal karma accumulated from past lives. We shouldn't think of these as something negative, but rather as something very dynamic that if imbalanced can create problems in the mind, energy, and body. Each one has its positive and negative aspects. For example, the hyper-mobility of the wind humor that can bring stress and anxiety is also a source of great creativity. The heat of the bile humor that can flare up as aggression is also the basis for a very clear and sharp mind; and the heaviness of the phlegm humor that brings slowness and resistance to change is also the root of stability and calmness.

Generally one or two humors dominate in most individuals while some people have a more even balance of the three. This is called our 'typology' which is our basic constitutional make-up and does not change dramatically during our lifetime. As we age and journey through life, different circumstances can cause these *nyepas* to become more significantly imbalanced which we refer to as 'pathology.' It is important to make dietary and lifestyle choices which help to balance our constitutional typology rather than put us into a

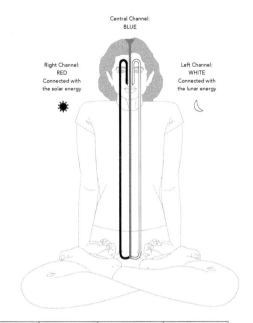

	Right Channel རོ་མ་ roma	Center Channel དབུ་མ་ uma	Left Channel ཀྱང་མ་ kyangma
Energy	Solar	Neutral	Lunar
Color	Red	Blue	White
Emotion	Anger Aversion	Desire Attachment	Ignorance Delusion
Humor	Bile མཁྲིས་པ་ treepa	Wind རླུང་ loong	Phlegm བད་ཀན་ beken
Element	Fire	Wind	Water & Earth
Animal	Snake	Rooster	Pig
	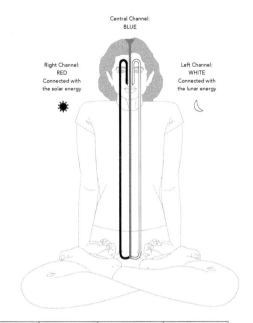		

state of further imbalance. As an example, if one has a constitutional predominance of wind (*loong*), living for prolonged periods of time in a dry and windy environment could over-stimulate this wind and potentially cause wind-related health problems that could be avoided by living in a different location or climate. Pathology can be subtle or gross, experienced as mild discomfort or may potentially manifest over time as severe disease. This depends on the strength of one's system as well as karmic and other conditions, some of which are not in our control.

The three humors and their corresponding three poisons also have an association with the three main energy channels in our body: the right (red) solar channel is connected with the bile humor and the mental poison of anger or aggression. This makes sense, since the liver and gallbladder are on the right side of our body and the bile organs are the organs connected with the fire element in Tibetan medicine. The left (white) lunar channel is connected with the phlegm humor and the poison of confusion, and the central (blue) neutral channel is connected with the wind humor and our attachment and desires. Cleaning out these three channels through the ninefold 'dead' or stale winds purification breathing exercise thus offers enormous benefits on a physical, energetic, and mental level.

In the tantric Buddhist teachings it is said that a poison can become medicine if you know how to use it, and there are highly sophisticated methods taught for skillfully working with the mental poisons so that they may be deeply understood and transformed into wisdom. These kinds of deeply transformative practices can be dangerous if one doesn't have a proper foundation or stability of mind. Physical yoga practices or breathing exercises such as this one are safe ways to help these 'poisons' move and be released in a healthy way so that they don't build up inside and cause harm to oneself, while at the same time preventing the need for them to be expressed outwardly in a way that is harmful to others.

There are several varieties of the ninefold purification breathing which involve more or less elaborate hand movements and positions. Taught here is one variety that I like very much because it incorporates a movement of the arms that supports a more clear visualization of the breath moving through the three channels and helps to coordinate mind, breath and bodily movement. At the beginning it might be challenging to remember these movements, but with practice it becomes very simple.

In addition to doing this breathing as a preliminary step to the Nejang Yoga practice, it is also very beneficial to do it first thing in the morning to clean your energy channels before starting your day, as well as at night before going to sleep in order to calm and relax the mind to promote more restful sleep. Good sleep is one of the primary contributors to good health and longevity and I recommend that people who suffer from insomnia spend a few minutes doing this breathing exercise before going to bed. Cleaning the channels in this way before going to sleep also brings more clarity to the dreaming state so it is very useful for anyone who is practicing Dream Yoga or trying to cultivate the skill of lucid dreaming. Those who experience anxiety can try doing this exercise at any time thoughout the day when symptoms arise.

Empty Body and Empty Channels Meditation

Before beginning the ninefold purification breathing, while seated with the spine straight in the sevenfold posture of Vairocana, meditate on your own body as empty. See yourself as a hollow shell, full of light, like a hologram. You have no organs, no bones, no muscles, no flesh, no blood. Empty yourself of all the things that you normally identify as your physical body and which have the potential to cause or experience pain or to get sick. If you have no liver, you cannot have liver problems, if no head, no headaches! See yourself as a light body. This luminous essence is the true nature of your body and also of your mind and with this meditation practice, we help bring ourselves back to this natural state.

Inside of this empty light-body of ours, we then visualize the three main energy channels in our subtle body (as pictured on p. 90). The central channel is blue and luminous, hollow like a bamboo tube. The two lateral channels, also hollow tubes of light, originate at our nostrils, wrap up into our skull, and travel down alongside the central channel, joining it four fingerwidths below the navel. Visualize the right channel as red and luminous and the left channel as bright white. Try not only to visualize, but also to feel these subtle channels in your body.

After visualizing the three channels inside our hollow body, we clean them out with the ninefold purification breathing practice. If your nostrils are blocked, blow your nose before beginning. If you are too congested to breath through your nostrils, you can breathe through your mouth.

To start, inhale deeply, then exhale completely through both nostrils.

1. Close the left nostril with the left index finger, and inhale while bringing the right index finger towards the top of the head. Draw pure, five-colored rainbow light in through the right nostril, bringing it down the right channel as your finger descends along the right channel, leading the energy downwards. When the finger reaches the level of the navel, suspend the breath, turn the hand upward, and guide the energy up the left channel with the finger. When the right finger reaches the level of the nose, close the right nostril with the right index finger. Release the left index finger from the left nostril and slowly exhale all impurities of anger and imbalances of the bile humor in the form of red smoke from the left nostril. If you are a very visual person, you can also imagine that little snakes (the symbol of anger) are expelled out of your left nostril with the exhale.

2. Reverse the process by inhaling pure rainbow light through the left nostril, using the left index finger to trace the energy down the left channel to the navel, then hold the breath and guide the energy up the right channel. When the left finger reaches the level of the nose, close the left nostril with the left finger, release the right finger from the right nostril, and exhale all impurities of ignorance and delusion and imbalances of the phlegm humor as whitish-grey smoke from the right nostril. You can also imagine little pigs (the symbol of confusion) being exhaled out of the right nostril. Rest the left hand on the left knee. (Both hands are now down on both knees.)

3. Inhale through both nostrils, guiding the energy down both side channels with the index fingers of both hands. Visualize rainbow light cleansing all three channels. When the fingers reach the level of the navel, drop the index fingers so that they point towards the root. Suspend the breath and trace the fingers upwards again, guiding this time with the wrists. When both hands reach the level of the nose, exhale all impurities of attachment and imbalances of the wind humor as dark bluish smoke from both nostrils. You can also imagine small roosters (the symbol of desire and attachment) being expelled out of both nostrils as you breathe out.[17]

17. In theory the central channel contains only wisdom winds and is totally pure, so therefore does not need to be 'cleaned'. This remains a subject of debate, however, as some tantric commentators claim that there are karmic winds in the central channel as well. Nevertheless, for the purpose of the exercise, when we do this cycle of breathing we can imagine cleaning the central channel along with the two lateral channels as well.

Try not to be tense or rigid as you move your arms. The more loose and relaxed the movement of the body, the more freely the energies will flow in the channels and the more relaxed your mind will feel as you do the exercise.

These three breaths form one cycle. Repeat the sequence three times to complete the nine purification breaths. Though this breath is called the 'ninefold' breathing, it is very good to repeat this breathing for several minutes, more than nine times. Actually, in the Tibetan language, the word *gu* or *gupa*, meaning 'nine' also means 'countless' and so when Tibetans say to do something 'nine' times, it generally means that it is something very beneficial that you should do many times!

Vajra Chanting

After cleaning the nostrils and the three channels with the ninefold purification breathing practice, the next preliminary breathing exercise is called "Vajra Chanting". This "chanting" is not a vocalized chanting, but refers to the subtle sound of the breath which naturally produces the mantra of OM AH HUNG, the three syllables corresponding to the three parts of our breathing: inhalation, retention and exhalation. According to Vajrayana Buddhism, these three syllables represent the enlightened qualities of Body, Speech Energy and Mind of all the Buddhas, or on a more subtle level our channels, winds and drops (*tsa, loong, thiglé*) that we learned about previously.

To do this breathing practice, sit with your spine straight but relaxed and as you breathe in, hear the very subtle sound of the mantra OM while visualizing a bright white light entering into your body through your nostrils. Then gently retain the breath, hearing and feeling the subtle vibration of the sound of AH and visualizing that the white light transforms into red and expands, filling the whole body with a brilliant red light. As you breathe out this red light turns to blue and leaves your body through the nostrils with the gentle sound of the syllable HUNG.

Begin this exercise by inhaling slowly to the count of five, then gently holding the breath for the count of three and exhaling to the count of four. As you become more comfortable with this exercise, you can train in increasing the duration of the breath retention so that it becomes the longest part of this threefold breathing cycle. This exercise is very calming to the nervous system, and as we have seen, slowing down and retainining the breath in this way is also an excellent rejuvenation or anti-aging practice.

Nejang Breathing: Partial Vase Breathing

The basic breathwork for Nejang practice is a partial vase breathing that involves a gentle breath retention. Imagine that there is a vase inside your lower abdomen that is open at the top at the level of the navel and fills up your belly. As you inhale, inhale very slowly and smoothly, as if you are slowly drawing an arrow until the bow is very taut. Visualize the breath coming through the two nostrils and into the two lateral channels , filling up the 'vase' in the lower abdomen. Once you have inhaled fully, retain the breath for as long as comfortable, drawing up the anus muscles and pushing down the breath from above so that the breath stays low and does not fill up the upper chest. After retaining the breath for as long as is comfortable, exhale quickly as if you are releasing the arrow, shooting the breath out of the nostrils. When you exhale, only approximately thirty percent of the breath should be released while the rest remains in the vase. The reason for this is that as you exhale, your breath separates into two parts - only the grossest part of our wind energy is expelled through the nostrils while the most subtle and pure part of the breath stays inside the vase. As you repeat this breath cycle many times, your vase slowly gets filled drop by drop with this pure wind energy, increasing your strength and vitality, charging up your inner battery. Practice this simple breathing exercise several times, retaining the breath only for as long as is comfortable. The spiritual significance of the transformation of karmic winds into wisdom winds through breath retention was explained in Chapter One on the Energetic Body. It takes a lot of time and dedicated practice to completely transform the karmic winds into wisdom winds, but through this kind of breathing, we can begin the process.

Combining Nejang Exercises with Yogic Breath Retention

It is during the breath retention portion of the breathing technique described above that each Nejang exercise is performed. In the Nejang practice, you combine each of the twenty four exercises with this kind of breathing in order to gather the force of the karmic winds which are drawn into the central channel through the breath retention, so that this energy may then be propelled back out into the two lateral channels and subsequently into all the 72,000 branch channels. At our level, we are not yet able to completely transform all of our karmic winds into wisdom winds, however in Nejang practice we can still use the force of these untransformed karmic winds to open up our channels. Knotted channels are like tubes through which air cannot pass and by pushing the karmic winds through the channels we can open and untie the knots so that the *loong* energy can flow more freely.

Contraindications for Breath Retention

Although yogic breath retention has many health benefits, it is not appropriate for everyone. Pregnant women should only do very short breath retentions and in general should practice the Nejang exercises in a very gentle and comfortable way. Likewise, elderly people or those with high blood pressure should not hold the breath for long. If you feel any kind of discomfort or symptoms from doing this kind of breathing, consult with your instructor. Practicing the Nejang exercises without the breath retention or with a very short retention is still very effective.

Bumpachen

Bumpachen (བུམ་པ་ཅན།) meaning 'the great vase,' is the root of all Tibetan yogic exercises and traditionally is considered a very secret teaching. I had to wait two years to receive this instruction from my root guru, Ani Ngawang Gyaltsen. Ani Ngawang Gyaltsen was my main teacher in Lhasa, a nun who transmitted to me the practices of the Longchen Nyingthig tradition, as well as the Six Yogas and Ati Yoga. She is also the one who taught me Nejang. In Tibet, once you receive instruction in *bumbachen* you have to do a 100 day retreat, or if you are not able to do strict retreat, you still need to complete the practice consistently for 100 days. If you do retreat, you only do *bumpachen* in that retreat, and that way you really get the best results from the practice. With my teacher's permission, I teach this practice more openly to my students, and also on occasion to my patients because it is simple, practical, and profound.

In addition to all the spiritual benefits of this practice, as a doctor I also value it for its great health benefits. *Bumpachen* is an excellent practice for treating *mazhupa* or indigestion (considered to be the root cause of all health problems in Tibetan medicine) since it increases metabolic heat. *Bumpachen* is also very good for both male and female reproductive issues and beneficial for menopausal women experiencing hot flashes. Following the principle that "like cures like" the heat generated through *bumpachen* practice can be an antidote for hot flashes. Most importantly, *bumpachen* is also a real antidote for chronic fatigue. Through this simple practice we can charge up our internal 'batttery' to avoid becoming depleted. We create a strong engine inside of us that prevents us from becoming fatigued, guarding us against the subsequent physical and psychological health problems arising from our exhaustion.

Emotionally, *bumpachen* is a powerful mood regulator. This

has something to do with happy hormones, like serotonin that we discussed earlier. We have a whole nervous system in our gut called the enteric nervous system (ENS), commonly referred to as our second brain, which is why there is such a connection between healthy digestion and our mood. Approximately ninety percent of the body's serotinin is actually produced in our digestive tract and becomes activated and released as we churn our bellies in the *bumpachen* practice. A weak digestive system is not only the root of other physical issues but can strongly influence our mental health in a similar way to how fasting can have an effect on our overall mental and physical wellbeing..

When the Buddha Shakyamuni left his palace to seek enlightenment he spent six years engaged in extreme ascetic practices. Depriving himself of food he became extremely emaciated as can be seen in some statues and paintings in which he is depicted with a hollowed out abdomen. Through this practice he completely changed the chemicals in his brain and body. Later

With my teacher the Yogini Ani Ngawang Gyaltsen, who taught me bumpachen and Nejang Yoga as well as transmitted to me the teachings of Ati Yoga, Mahamudra, and the Six Yogas, when I was a medical student in Lhasa, Tibet.

he abandoned this practice and promoted instead the path of the Middle Way, but it was an important step in his evolution and transformation. According to Tibetan Medicine, fasting (expecially extreme versions of it) is not appropriate for all people, but it can be a powerful spiritual practice and can also have healing effects if done appropriately and according to one's individual constitution type. In general fasting is very hard for the first few days, but afterwards many people notice that they feel very light and happy without cravings for food and other things. This is because of the increased production of serotinin in the gut which gets released in the blood bringing a sense of sustained happiness. *Bumpachen* can have a similar effect if practiced regularly and to enhance its effects, it is best to practice on an empty stomach.

Bumpachen is not one of the actual 24 Nejang exercises, but can be done as a daily practice in conjunction with the other exercises or as a general preparatory exercise. It is similar to the partial vase breathing described above, except it adds one more important step before the exhale, which is called 'churning,' that is, forcibly pressing and moving the retained *loong* around in the belly.

The four steps of *bumpachen* practice are:

1)   Inhale - རྔུབ། *(Ngup)*
2)   Hold - དགང་། *(Gang)*
3)   Churn - གཞིལ། *(Shil)*
4)   Shoot - འཕང་ས། *(Pang)*

To do the practice, inhale slowly and smoothly, then while holding breath inside the vase below the navel, rotate the belly clockwise and then counterclockwise. Then exhale and shoot the breath out of the nostrils quickly. Start by rotating the belly seven times clockwise, then seven times counterclockwise. With practice, as you are able to comfortably retain your breath for longer periods of time, you can increase the number of rotations. However you should not put too much strain on yourself and it is better to choose a number of rotations that you can repeat for several breath-cycles in a row without having to stop due to fatigue. By turning the belly in this way, you are churning the karmic winds into wisdom winds, in the same way that milk is churned into butter. The more that the karmic winds get transformed into wisdom winds, the easier it will be to hold the breath for more extended periods of time. Doing *bumpachen* practice is like slowly blowing through a straw: as you blow, the straw (our channels) get unblocked so that energy can flow freely.

Churning the belly naturally unblocks the nostrils. The nasal passages are very important because according to Tibetan subtle anatomy teachings, inside our nose there is a channel called the 'king of all channels'. When our nostrils are blocked, even just a little bit, this puts a big strain on the body because the breath cannot flow freely so it's important for the nostrils to stay open. With orgasm (and also with sneezing) this king channel inside the nose opens up naturally and in that moment there is no possibility for sadness or any of the afflictive emotions. Opening the nostrils through *bumpachen* has a similarly powerful effect, improving our mood automatically because the stress caused by the blocked nasal passages has been removed.

There are different names for the *bumpachen* breathing, depending on how many rotations you are able to do per breath cycle. Once you are able to rotate the belly (clockwise and couterclockwise) thirty five times, then you have accomplished what is called 'small vase' (*bum chung*). Traditionally, only when you have reached the level of the small vase are you eligible to receive instruction in Tibetan yoga practices. When you can rotate the belly fifty five times this is called the 'medium vase' (*bum dring*) and when you can rotate seventy five times, you have accomplished the 'big vase' *(bum chen)*.   It takes many years of dedicated practice to accomplish this level, so please do not attempt this at the early stages of your practice. Begin with seven rotations, increase to ten, twelve, and so on at a slow and steady pace. As you progress in this practice and learn to control your energy you will in turn gain greater control of your emotions and eventually a very stable and sustained experience of joy in the mind.

You can practice *bumpachen* at any time of day, but not directly after eating. For many people practicing *bumpachen* is very invigorating, and for them it is best to practice in the morning since this increased energy and clarity is useful in the daytime but could potentially disrupt one's nighttime sleep patterns if done too late in the day. For others *bumpachen* is very calming and can also be very tiring, so in this case it may be better to practice in the evening when you are able to rest after. Experiment for yourself to see what time of day is best for you to practice. For most people, *bumpachen* has an invogorating but at the same time very calming effect and can be done at any time of the day.

Contraindications for Bumpachen

There are a few contraindications to practicing *bumpachen*: you should not practice if you are pregnant, have high blood pressure, heart or lung disease. Additionally, it can be dangerous for elderly people if they are not used to this practice, as they might hold the breath and then not be able to breathe out. If older people do Nejang, it is better that they do not do *bumpachen* or strong breath retention. Sometimes *bumpachen* can create some issues with *sog dzin loong* (the first root *loong*, 'life sustaining wind'), which can lead to dizziness, a feeling of not being able to control the mind, or possibly even hallucinations. This is rare but it can happen, so it is important to pay attention to how you feel when you do this practice and to start slowly, stopping if there are any adverse effects. In general, if *bumpachen* is practiced correctly with proper instruction, it is a safe and effective practice both for maintaining health and for spiritual growth. For this reason I teach this practice in many of my courses and have also authorized teachers of Nejang Yoga who are well trained in the practice to instruct others. I have explained the practice here for general information purposes, but *bumpachen* cannot be learned properly solely from a book. Before beginning this practice, it is important to receive proper in-person instruction from a qualified teacher.

In the past, the three year retreat that the Tibetan tradition is so known for was based on *bumpachen* and nothing else. Yogis did not do many different practices, only this vase breathing and through this training they were able to completely transform their karmic winds into wisdom winds, and to rest as a result in a joyful state free of conceptual thoughts, completely transformed physically, energetically, and mentally. The reason that this process takes three years (or more precisely three years, three months, and three days) is that in our ordinary breathing process, every 32th breath that we take is a breath of wisdom wind. After thirty one karmic wind breaths, all of us take one wisdom wind breath. The average person takes between twelve and twenty breaths per minute, so in approximately two minutes, one cycle of thirty two breaths is completed and we have breathed one wisdom wind breath. This means that if we hold our breath for two minutes, we can send the thirty one karmic winds into that last wisdom wind breath, transforming those thirty one breaths. Three years, three months, and three days is the exact amount of time that it takes to transform all of the karmic winds of a 100 year lifespan through the practice of *bumpachen*. By condensing a lifetime of wisdom winds into this three year period, yogis and yoginis attempted to attain complete enlightenment, freeing themselves completely of their karma. This retreat was traditionally practiced by young children and completed before the age of sixteen.[18]

Bumpachen and Astrology

Our sixty four petaled navel chakra called the Chakra of Manifestation (*trulpey khorlo*) is connected with astrology, each petal connecting to a particular planetary energy. This means that by working with the navel chakra through *bumpachen*, you can free yourself from any astrological influences and even influence the planets! Those who do not practice various yogas or go through life less mindfully and more habitually are thus understood to be more subject to the constraining influences of the planets, stars, and outer environmental forces. The practice of tantric yoga, however, allows us to gain control over outer elements and influences by controlling their corresponding energies inside the inner universe of our own subtle body. While astrology is important, we should understand that the planets can only influence twenty percent of our experience, since only one of our five chakras is connected with astrology. By mastering that chakra, we can also be totally free of astrological influences and in control of our own lives and energy.

---

18. According to Tibetan tradition, the white *thiglé*, which is inherited from the father at conception, is said to build up from the age of eight to sixteen. The red *thiglé*, which comes from the mother, develops in turn from between the age of sixteen and thirty two. The period between the ages of eight and sixteen when the white *thiglé* is building is said to be the optimum time to engage in *tsaloong* training. After thirty two, most people's channels become knotted and weakened, leading to a decline in overall levels of vitality and to a depletion of one's *thiglé* which makes intensive *tsaloong* practices more difficult and less effective.

Chapter 4: The Actual Practice

General Instructions

24 Exercises & Final Relaxation

Steps of Nejang Practice

The Actual Practice

General Instructions

Sit in the seven-point posture of Vairocana. For each exercise, inhale and hold the breath while compressing the energy at the navel. Perform the exercise while retaining the breath, then exhale.

Depending on the length of your breath retention and the speed at which you like to do the exercise, repeat each movement three, seven, or twenty one times per breath. Do not force yourself to retain the breath beyond your level of comfort. As you become more trained, you may increase the length of your breath retention little by little. The speed at which you perform the exercises is a personal choice and depends upon the condition of your body and the aim of your practice. Each exercise may be done in a slow and gentle manner, or in a more vigorous manner which will generate more heat.

In the following pages, the first line of the English (in bold) is a direct translation of the original Tibetan text above. This is followed by a more elaborate explanation of how to actually do the exercise with some modifications when applicable. As mentioned in the Introduction, the tantric indications comes from Butön Rinchen Drup's original Nejang text whereas the medical indications are later elaborations by Tibetan doctors with some notes from my own practical experience in using these exercises with patients.

To learn more about the Tibetan medical indications as well as the significance of the specific points massaged in these exercises, please refer to my books, "The Tibetan Book of Health: Sowa Rigpa, the Science of Healing" (Chenatsang 2017) and "Sowa Rigpa Points: Point Study in Traditional Tibetan Medicine" (Chenagtsang and Nguyen 2017).

A note on the sense organs: As explained in Chapter Two on the benefits of Nejang, the five sense organs are very important in Tibetan Medicine because symptoms in these outer sense organs can be indicators of imbalances of the solid and hollow inner organs. The sense organs can be used both for treatment and for diagnosis: exercising and massaging the sense organs can help to maintain health in the inner organs, and observing and asking questions about the function of the sense organs can help the Tibetan doctor to better assess what is happening with the inner organs. Exercises one to four and fourteen are Nejang exercises that work directly with the sense organs in order to influence their corresponding inner organs. Additional images are included that show how the sense organs are used diagnostically by Tibetan doctors to assess not only the particular solid and hollow organ associated with that sense organ, but other organs as well. In the same way that the Kalachakra teaches that the human body is a microcosm of the larger universe, each small part of the human body, such as the ear, can be viewed as a representation of the entire phyical body.

Modifications: Nejang Yoga is designed to be accessible to people of all ages and physical conditions. Certain modifications are included in this book. The majority of the twenty four Nejang exercises can be done on chair and do not require the practitioner to be seated on the floor. I have taught this practice to many patients who are paralyzed and have shown them how to visualize doing the exercise on or with the affected side that they cannot physically move. Even if the body cannot do the exercise, this visualization can help to restore brain function. If someone cannot reach their ear to massage it as instructed in the first exercise, they can reach as far as possible and simply imagine the rest. For elderly people it is very important to stay busy, to keep moving and to stimulate the senses, and doing even extremely modified versions of these exercises can serve this purpose and be very helpful.

Ear

Reproductive Organs

Urinary Bladder

Kidneys

1. དང་པོ་རྣ་བ་གཡས་པ་མཉེ། རྣ་བ་གཡོན་པའང་དེ་བཞིན་ནོ།

First: Massage the right ear, then in the same way the left.

Massage the right ear with the left hand, keeping the face and eyes pointing straight ahead. Make sure to massage all parts of the ear, including the tragus, and fold the ear. Exhale and then switch sides. The ears should redden from the increase of heat and blood flow.

Modification: You may also cross the arms and massage both ears simultaneously.

Tantric: Pacifies the wind in the muscles and the skin complexion.

Medical: Balances the kidneys, gives stability to the spine, and strengthens the urinary bladder and reproductive organs. Also balances the phlegm humor.

According to Tibetan Medicine, the tragus (the small piece of thick cartilege of the external ear in front of the ear canal) is associated with memory. Massaging and softening this part of the ear is a simple way to enhance memory.

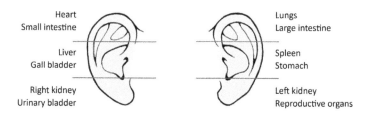

The ears as a whole are most directly connected to the kidney and bladder function, but Tibetan doctors will also observe specific parts of the ear to diagnose the health of all of the solid and hollow organs as pictured above. Massaging all parts of the ear thoroughly can benefit all of the organs as well as all the vertebra of the entire spine.

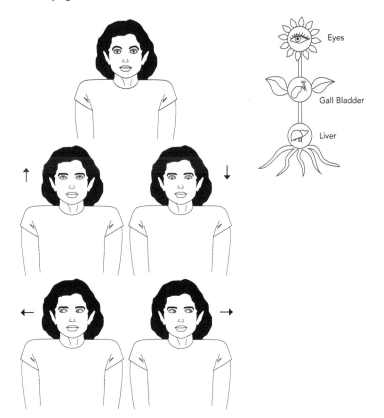

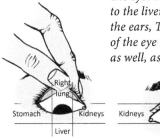

The eyes as a whole are most directly connected to the liver and gallbladder function, but like the ears, Tibetan doctors observe specific parts of the eye to diagnose the health of other organs as well, as seen here.

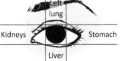

2. གཉིས་པ་མིག་གཉིས་རབ་ཏུ་བསྒྲད་ལ། ཁྱོགས་བཞི་དག་ཏུ་རྡང་པར་བལྟ།།

Second: Opening the two eyes widely gaze into the four directions.

First, open the eyes widely and look straight ahead. Second, look up and down (seven times slowly or twenty one times quickly). Third, look to the right and the left (seven times slowly or twenty one times quickly). Fourth, rotate the eyes clockwise and then counterclockwise. (Perform one movement per breath)

Tantric: Heals the eyes and balances lacrimation.

Medical: Balances the liver, gall bladder, pancreas, and bile humor.

For patients who have coordination issues and difficulty doing this exercise, tell them to use their index finger to guide the motion of their eyes. By focusing on the tip of their finger, it will be easier to control the movement of their eyes. Exercising the eyes is important in improving coordination and maintaining proper brain function.

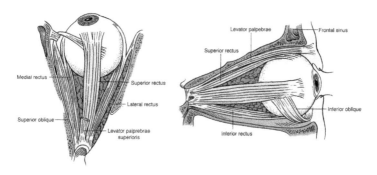

Movement of the eye in different directions is made possible by a variety of muscles as seen in the image above.

3. གསུམ་པ་སྣ་རྩེ་མཉེ་ཞིང་འཐེན།།

Third: Massage and pull the tip of the nose.

Begin at the root of the nose, massaging towards the tip. Repeat movement three times per breath. On the third movement, massage, pinch and release the tip of the nose.

Tantric: Cures small intestine pain.

Medical: Balances the lungs and large intestine, as well as the phlegm and wind humors.

Increasing blood flow to the nose with this exercise is also useful for people who have sinitus and allergies. As we learned in the section on *bumpachen*, keeping the nasal passages open is extremely important, because the subtle strain on the body that comes from impeding the flow of natural breathing has implications for one's mood and stress level and even spiritually since a very important energetic channel is located in the nose.

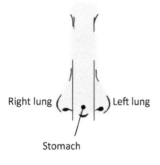

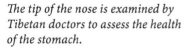

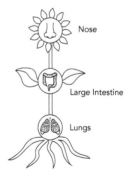

The tip of the nose is examined by Tibetan doctors to assess the health of the stomach.

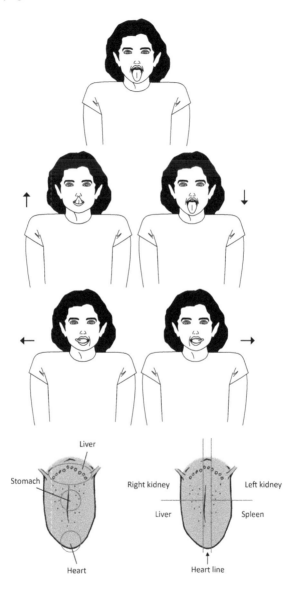

Liver
Stomach
Heart

Right kidney
Left kidney
Liver
Spleen
Heart line

4. བཞི་པ་ལྕེ་བརྐྱངས་ཕྱོགས་བཞི་དངས།།

Fourth: Stick out the tongue and stretch it in the four directions.

First stretch the tongue out and down and hold. Second, stretch the tongue up (towards the the tip of the nose) and down (towards the chin) seven times per breath. Third, stretch the tongue to the right and the left seven times.

Tantric. Good for brain disorders.

Medical: Disorders of heart, small intestine, emotional blockages such as sadness, depression, lack of memory. Balances the wind humor.

The 'heart' refers to both our cardiovascular organ and to our emotional and spiritual heart. For people who suffer from depression, anxiety, or other psycho-emotional issues, exercising the tongue should be a daily, essential practice. This exercise is also an important practice to do post-stroke.

I had a 92 year old Italian patient who had lost his sense of taste. He could not move his body much so I taught him how to do this tongue yoga and he loved it. Over time his taste was restored through this simple exercise.

Left: While the tongue is most directly connected to the heart and small intestine, observing the tongue is a very important diagnostic technique used by the Tibetan (and Chinese) doctor to better understand the health of the patient as a whole. Color, moistness/ dryness, shape and texture are all observed and specific sections of the tongue are examined to give information to the physician about each of the inner organs.

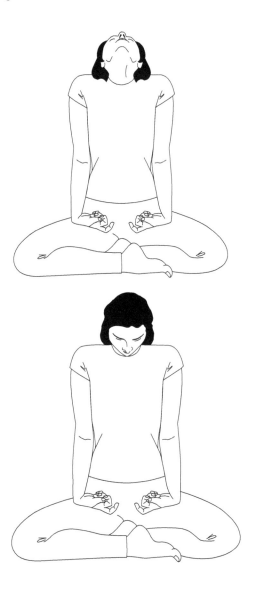

5. ལྥ་པ་མགོ་སྒུག་ལན་གསུམ་རྒྱ།།

Fifth: Nod the head three times

Slowly tuck the chin into the chest and then lift the chin up, stretching the neck open (three to five times per breath), being careful not to strain your neck.

Modification: You may hold the back of your neck with both hands when stretching back in order to protect the neck if sensitive. If your neck is very strong, you may do this exercise more quickly and vigorously which makes you feel very clear headed.

Tantric: Balances abdominal bloating (stomach and spleen energies).

Medical: Balances the life-sustaining wind, cures headache, migraine, improves memory, clears the mind, relaxes the internal organs.

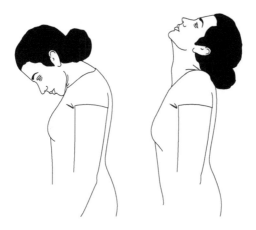

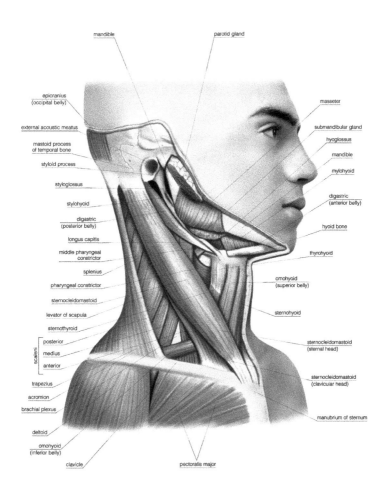

The muscles of the neck activated in exercises 5, 9, and 15.

To locate the crown point, place your thumb directly between your two eyes and reach your middle finger as far back as possible. Rub around the area where your middle finger reaches to find the sensitive point.

The crown point lies at the junction between the right and left hemispheres of the brain. Our scalp consists of five layers as seen in the image above.

6. རྡུག་པ་སྤྱི་གཙུག་དྲག་ཏུ་མཉེ།།

Sixth: Vigorously massage the crown of the head.

Use the palm of your hand to strongly rub the crown of your head. Alternatively, keep your hand in the vajra fist and massage the crown with the ulnar side of your palm.

Tantric: Helps stiffness of limbs, both for difficulty in extension and contraction.

Medical: Pacifies all winds, calms the mind, reduces over-thinking. Helps breathing, stimulates circulation in the brain.

I call this crown location the tranquilizer point because it is the most calming point on the body, good for sleep, relaxation, and also heart conditions (according to Tibetan Medicine, balding on the top of the head in the area of the crown point is a sign of a sensitive heart).

Along with the center of the palms of the hands and the centers of the soles of the feet, the crown is one of the five "gates of the *loong* (wind energy)." Massaging or applying warm oil to these points is especially powerful in relaxing symptoms associated with excess wind, such as anxiety and insomnia.

The crown as well as all of the other points on the head massaged in Nejang Yoga are important points to activate in order to counteract the onset of neurodegenerative diseases. The brain can accumulate toxins and pathogens which inhibits blood flow, thereby affecting the memory. Stimulating these points helps to restore blood flow to the brain. If elderly patients are not able to reach and massage their own heads, you can do it for them.

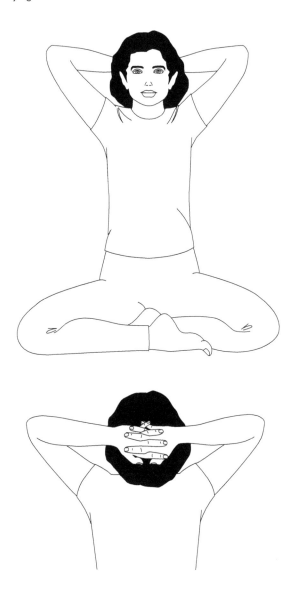

7. བདུན་པ་ལག་སྟེལ་ལྤག་པ་མཉེ།།

Seventh: Interlace the hands and massage the back of the head.

Interlace your fingers behind your head and massage the occipital region by rubbing up and down and then squeezing the heels of the hands together (several times per breath)

Tantric: Stops loss of hair and beard.

Medical. Strengthens the eyes, kidneys, spleen. Helps headaches, relaxes the neck, and releases tension.

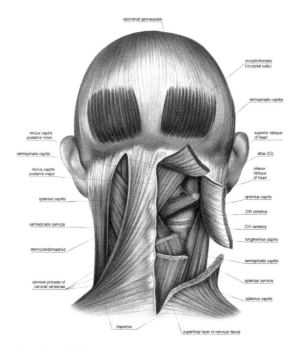

*Muscles of the occipital region of the back of the head.
These are important pressure points for releasing tension.*

8. བརྒྱད་པ་སྨིན་མཚམས་དྲག་ཏུ་མཉེ།།

Eighth: Vigorously massage in between the eyebrows.

Keeping your hand in the vajra fist rub the forehead strongly in between the eyebrows up and down using the ulnar side of your palm. Don't rub this point too strongly as the skin can be sensitive in this area.

Tantric: Heals bone problems.

Medical: Relaxes, clears and settles the mind, heals emotional troubles, balances the wind humor, helps sleep problems.

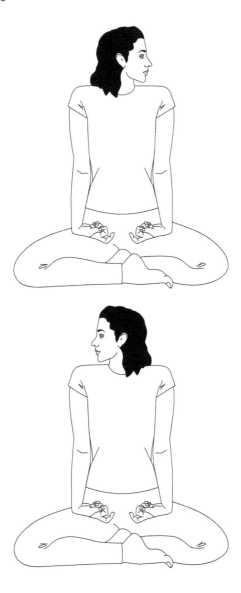

9. དགུ་པ་མགོ་བོ་གཡས་གཡོན་གཅུ།།

Ninth: Twist your head to the right and then the left.

Turn your head slowly to the right and then to the left ninety degrees. You may do it more quickly if your neck is strong, but be sure to turn your head completely in each direction.

Tantric: Heals tooth problems, and toothaches.

Medical: Strengthens the sense organs. Anti-headache and vertigo, improves memory.

(See exercise 5 for image of neck muscles activated by turning the head)

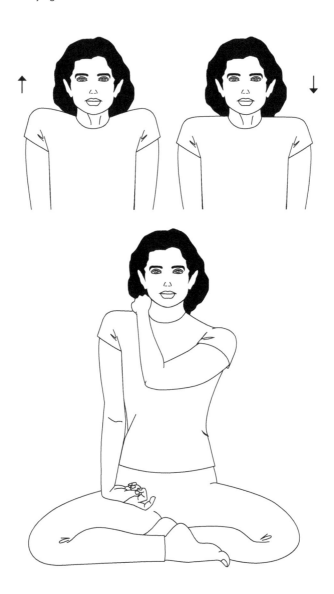

10. བཅུ་པ་ཕྲག་པ་མཉེ་གསིག་བསྐྱོད།།

Tenth: Massage, shake, and move the shoulders.

First massage each shoulder using the opposite hand; next shrug the shoulders to the ears and release (slowly or quickly shaking); then rotate the shoulders backwards and forwards; finally masssage and move the shoulders at the same time, using the fingers to exert pressure on the tender points while you move into the pressure. (Do each one of these steps per breath).

Modification: You may reverse the order of these movements by shrugging and shaking the shoulders first if it is painful to massage right away.

Tantric: Heals heart problems.

Medical: Releases shoulder tension, good for lung problems. Relaxes diaphragm to release tension and hiccups.

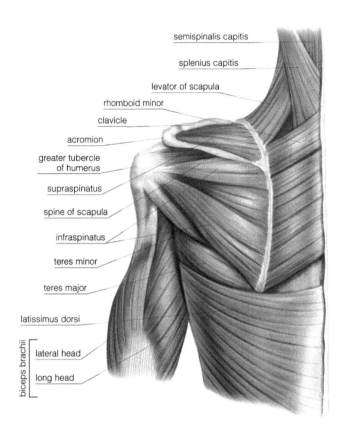

semispinalis capitis

splenius capitis

levator of scapula

rhomboid minor

clavicle

acromion

greater tubercle
of humerus

supraspinatus

spine of scapula

infraspinatus

teres minor

teres major

latissimus dorsi

biceps brachii

lateral head

long head

Shoulder muscles, front view.

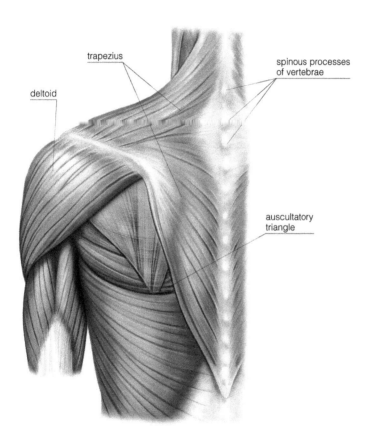

Shoulder muscles, back view.

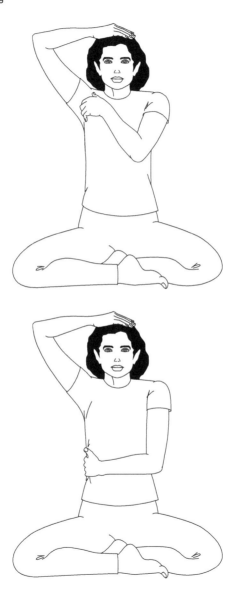

11. བཅུ་གཅིག་པ་མཆན་ཁུང་གཡས་གཡོན་མཉེ།།

Eleventh: Massage the right and left armpit.

Place the hand on the top of the head in order to open up the arm pit. Use the fingers to massage the right armpit, and then the left. Then rub up and down the side of the body from armpit to the waist vigorously.

Tantric. Heals eye problems.

Medical: Helps the lungs, liver, gall bladder, and kidney on the right. The left side helps heart, spleen, and kidneys. Releases pressure in the chest and helps coughing, also helps the lymphatic system.

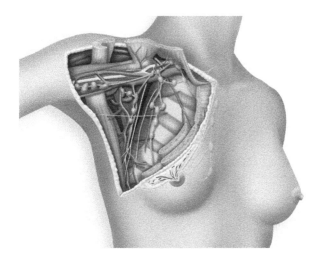

Illustration of the lymph nodes, muscle tissue, and blood vessels in this important region of the body.

12. བཅུ་གཉིས་ནུ་མ་མཉེ་ཞིང་བསྐྱོད།།

Twelfth: Massage and move the breasts.

Massage the breasts by rotating in one direction, then the opposite, then shaking up and down.

Tantric: Good for bile problems.

Medical: Pacifies all winds, calms the mind, treats the mind, as well as over-thinking. Helps breathing, stimulates circulation in the brain, helps breastfeeding women to produce milk.

I call the nipple the anger point - when you are angry,
instead of yelling at your partner, massage your nipples!
It is not recommended to pierce the nipple.

13. བཅུ་གསུམ་པ་སྟེ་བ་བསྐོར་ཞིང་སྤྲུག །

Thirteenth: Rotate and shake the navel.

Hold the vase breath and rotate the belly and lower back clockwise and then counter-clockwise. Begin with seven rotations in each direction per breath, increase the number of rotations as is comfortable. If you have back pain, move slowly.

This exercise resembles somewhat the movement of *bumpachen*, but whereas in *bumbachen* we are isolating and 'churning' the muscles of the belly, in this exercise we make larger rotations to work the back and spine.

Modification: Place your hands on your knees and rotate your belly and spine as explained above. Use the pressure on your knees to help you make larger more exaggerated movements of the back.

Tantric: Problems in the upper leg and stomach.

Medical: Improves digestion, increases metabolic fire, unblocks constipation. Builds up body energy. Excellent for backaches.

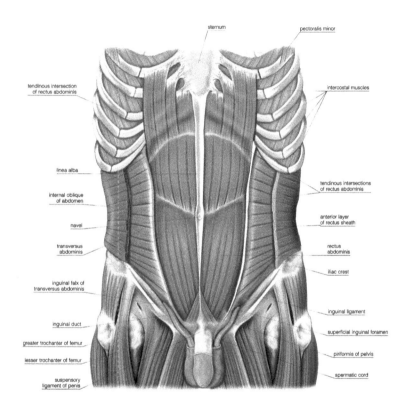

Abdominal muscles activated by this exercise.

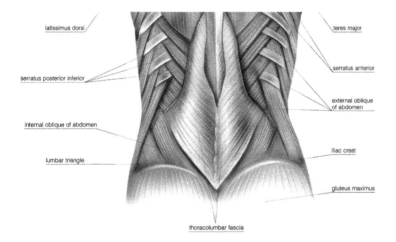

Back muscles activated by this exercise.

14. བཅུ་བཞི་ཁ་བསྡམས་དྲག་ཏུ་དབྱེ།།

Fourteenth: Seal the mouth shut and then forcefully open it.

Tightly purse the lips together and then slowly stretch the mouth open wide. Repeat three or seven times per breath.

Tantric: Good for stomach problems and abdominal pain.

Medical: Good for the stomach and spleen.

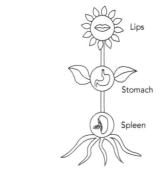

In addition to the stomach and spleen, the lips can also show the health or imbalance of the liver and gallbladder as indicated above.

15. བཙོ་ལྡ་མ་གྲིན་པ་གཅུ་ཞིང་མཉེ།།

Fifteenth: Twist and massage the neck.

Rotate the neck slowly clockwise and then counterclockwise. Hold the back of the neck and massage as you rotate the neck.

Modification: You can also rotate the neck without using the hands to massage as pictured below. Be careful not to strain the neck as you do so.

Tantric: Good for navel problems.

Medical: Releases tension in the neck, helps headaches, balances ascending wind which aids in breathing and asthma.

Modification

Try to imitate the look of birds taking a shower when you do this exercise. Shake vigorously!

16. བཅུ་དྲུག་སྙིང་ག་རག་ཏུ་སྤྲུགས།།

Sixteenth: Vigorously shake the heart.

Lean forwards, pivoting the whole torso, and "shake the heart". Repeat this movement, moving the torso down and up several times. On the last one, rock forwards, lift the buttocks, and drop down while exhaling strongly.

The last part of the exercise in which we drop down constitutes a mini '*bep*' (Tibetan 'jumping' practice). Refer to the footnote in exercise eighteen to learn more about the *bep*.

Modification: You may place your hands on your knees instead of in vajra fists and practice the exercise as above. You can also do this exercise in slow motion, twisting completely in each direction to thoroughly stretch out the side of the body.

Tantric: Good for constipation and difficult urination.

Medical: Releases tension in the internal organs.

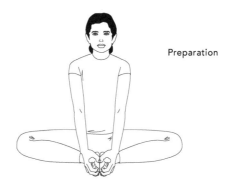

Preparation

Option 1

Option 2

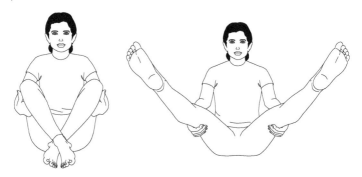

17. བཅུ་བདུན་འདོ་མས་གཉིས་རབ་ཏུ་བགྲད།།

Seventeenth: Thoroughly spread the two inner thighs.

Preparation: Sit straight with your feet together and knees open, lifting your knees up and down, stretching the inner thighs. Pull the feet only as close to your groin as is comfortable.

Exercise: Rock back and balance on your sit bones. Grab the thighs with knees bent and open and close the legs (See Option 1). Or bend the knees and cross the ankles then stretch the legs out. Alternating the which way in which you cross the ankles each time is helpful for increasing coordination. Exhale as you return to seated position in between each breath.

Modification: Perform the movement of the legs while lying on the back.

Tantric: Good for problems in the fontanelle.

Medical: Unblocks descending wind, regulates the lower excretions.

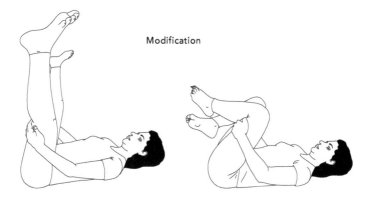

Modification

18. བཙོག་རྐྱང་བ་གཤང་ལམ་འབྱེད་འཛུམ་བྱ༎

Eighteenth: Constrict and release the anus.

Contract and pull up the anus seven or more times per breath, then exhale and release.

Tantric: Good for stomach cramps.

Medical: Increases metabolic heat, good for constipation, stimulates phlegm humor and balances the descending wind. Helps menstruation problems and ovarian cysts in women and helps the prostate in men. Good for incontinence in the elderly.

This exercise can also be combined with a 'bep', a 'jumping' exercise used in Tibetan trulkhor practices for releasing stuck energy in the channels. Inhale and constrict the anus, then lift off the floor and drop down seven times, exhaling after the last bep. Dropping on the floor with a little bit of force releases the stuck energy, but if you have back problems, it is better not to do the bep or to do it very gently.

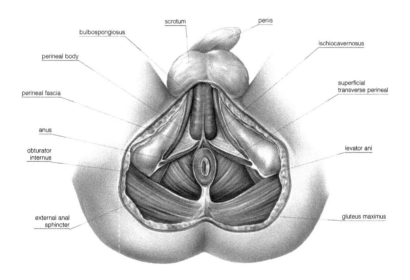

Male muscles of the perineum, exercise 18.

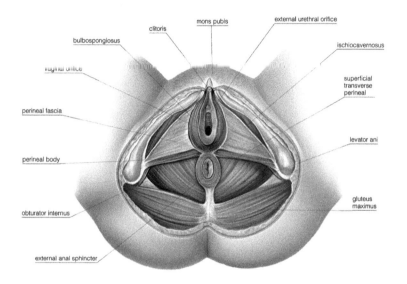

Female muscles of the perineum, exercise 18.

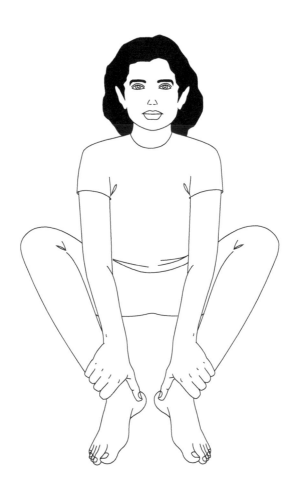

19. བཅུ་དགུ་པོ་ལ་གོང་ཚིགས་དུ་མཉེ།།

Nineteenth: Strongly massage the ankles.

Strongly rub and massage both ankles, fronts, backs, and sides; also tap.

Tantric: Cures lower back aches and pains.

Medical: Helps the kidneys, balances the menses, good for joint pain.

The ankles have many important acupuncture and moxibustion points. Be sure to rub, massage, and tap all areas on the front, back, and sides of the ankles to stimulate these points.

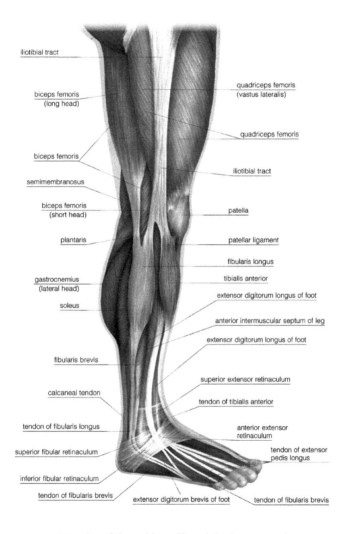

iliotibial tract

biceps femoris
(long head)

biceps femoris

semimembranosus

biceps femoris
(short head)

plantaris

gastrocnemius
(lateral head)

soleus

fibularis brevis

calcaneal tendon

tendon of fibularis longus

superior fibular retinaculum

inferior fibular retinaculum

tendon of fibularis brevis

quadriceps femoris
(vastus lateralis)

quadriceps femoris

iliotibial tract

patella

patellar ligament

fibularis longus

tibialis anterior

extensor digitorum longus of foot

anterior intermuscular septum of leg

extensor digitorum longus of foot

superior extensor retinaculum

tendon of tibialis anterior

anterior extensor
retinaculum

tendon of extensor
pedis longus

tendon of fibularis brevis

extensor digitorum brevis of foot

*Muscles of the ankle, calf, and thigh massaged
in exercises 19, 20, and 21.*

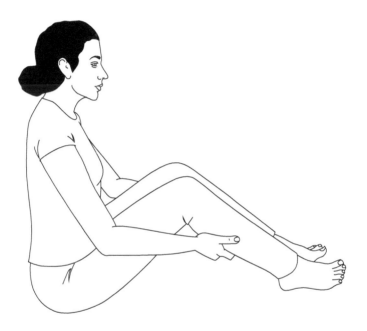

20. ཉི་ཤུ་བྱིན་པ་རབ་ཏུ་མཉེ།།

Twentieth: Thoroughly massage the calves.

Rub and massage the calves strongly. Also tap with loose fists or palms.

Tantric: Pacifies wind.

Medical: Balances the kidneys, opens the heart, releases fear, helps to prevent bad dreams. Good for panic attacks.

The point directly in the center of the calf is called the "fear point" and it is tender in many people.

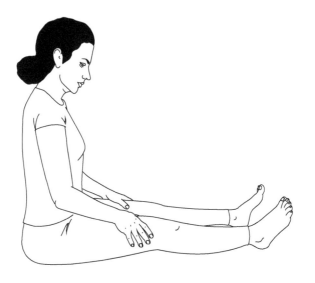

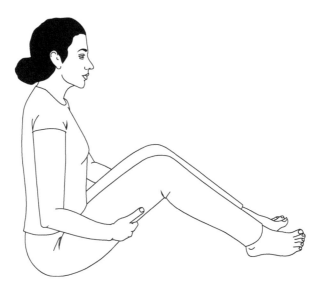

21. ཉེར་གཉིས་བརླ་གཉིས་རབ་ཏུ་མཉེ།།

Twenty-first: Thoroughly massage the two thighs.

Massage and rub both thighs, front, back, inside, and outside. Then tap with fists or palms. This exercise can be done with legs slightly bent or stretched out straight.

Tantric: Pacifies blood problems.

Medical: Pacifies hot-natured diseases, balances bile, stimulates circulation, strengthens the immune system and protects the body.

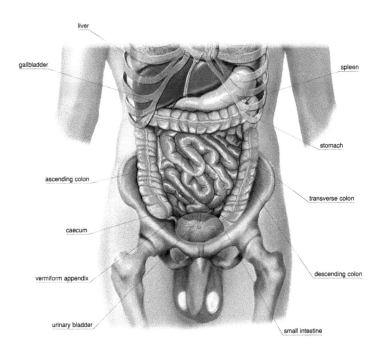

Abdominal organs.

22. ཉེར་གཉིས་ལྟེ་བ་རྒྱ་མཚོ་བསྐྱོད།།

Twenty second: Move the belly like the ocean.

Gyrate your belly vertically like a wave. Move the belly in a downwards direction, then repeat the movement in an upwards motion. This exercise is difficult at the beginning but becomes easier with regular practice.

Modification: If this exercise is difficult, place your hands on your belly, using your hands to help to initiate the movement in the abdomen. Also train the muscles by practicing simply drawing the navel in and out rapidly with the breath held in the lower abdomen.

Tantric: Releases muscle pains.

Medical: Increases metabolic heat, strengthens digestion, helps promote proper excretions. (The downward wave helps constipation, the upward wave helps diarrhea). Good for menstrual pain. If menstruation is delayed, practice the downward wave.

(See exercise thirteen for an image of the abdominal muscles activated by this exercise)

23. ཉེར་གསུམ་སྟག་མོའི་སྐྱུགས་སྟངས་བྱ།།

Twenty third: Vomit in the manner of a tiger.

Inhale and retain the breath, then lean forwards onto your hands and knees and arch and curve your spine three, seven (or twenty one times if doing the exercise quickly and vigorously), stretching your chin up and then tucking your chin into your chest. On the last movement, with your chin tucked in, curve the spine strongly, pulling the belly in and vomit "like a tiger". Stick out the tongue while exhaling and make noise.

Modificaiton: This exercise can also be done in a seated posture as pictured below.

Tantric: Unblocks the winds trapped inside the channels.

Medical: Releases emotions, helps problems of the phlegm humor. Good for abdominal pain and digestive problems.

(See exercise 13 for image of abdominal muscles activated by this exercise)

24. ཉེར་བཞི་ལུས་པོ་ཐམས་ཅད་མཉེ།།

Twenty fourth: Massage the whole body.

Tantric: Releases stiffness in the channels, and blockage of the winds.

Medical: Opens up the all-pervasive wind. Circulates the blood, wind energy, facilitates ease of motion in the whole body.

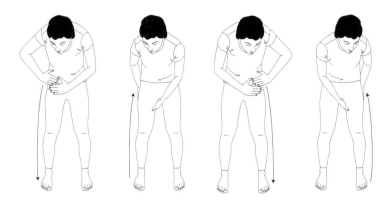

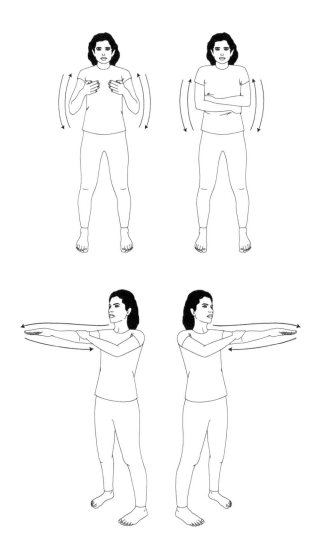

Inhale deeply into the belly and warm your your hands by rubbing them together vigorously, then while holding the breath in the abdomen rub each part of the body, twenty one times in this order:

1. Face
2. Top of Head
3. Back of Head
4. Neck
5. Shoulders
6. Lower Back
7. Legs (one at a time, down the front and up the back, stretching all the way down to the feet)
8. Torso
9. Ribs
10. Arms (one at a time, down the top to the finger tips, up the back)

After each body part, exhale and shake out the body before moving on to the next part.

Modifications:

Instead of exhaling after each movement, you can combine all of the the body parts listed above into a single breath. Take a very deep breath into the abdomen while rubbing and warming the hands, then rub each part of the body three times only, progressing through the entire sequence of movements. If it is too much to complete all the movements in one breath, take a breath halfway through and then complete the exercises on the second breath. Repeat the entire sequence three times at least and after the last one, shake the body while exhaling and repeating the syllable 'HA'. Keep repeating this last step, the 'HA shake', relaxing and invigorating the entire body.

This exercise can also be done from a seated position (on the floor or on a chair.) When rubbing the legs, stretch one leg out at a time and rub, then return to the basic seated posture.

This invigorating exercise is excellent to do first thing in the morning to wake up the body and all the channels or at any time during the day that you feel tired or when your mood is low. Kids also love to do this yoga!

Final Relaxation

After finishing your Nejang exercises, lie on your back and for a few minutes completely rest your body, heavy on the floor. Allow your breath to be completely natural and return to the Empty Body meditation that we began the practice with, seeing yourself as hollow and luminous.

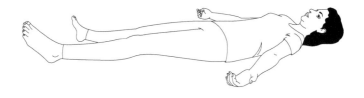

Steps of Nejang Practice

These numbers may help you to remember the steps of a complete Nejang Yoga practice:

4: Immeasurable Practice (Setting the intention)

7: fold Posture of Vairocana and Empty Body and Empty Channels Meditation

9: fold Purification Breathing Practice

3: Vajra Chanting (OM AH HUNG)

4: Bumpachen (Inhale, Hold, Churn, Shoot)

24: Nejang Yoga Exercises

Dedication of Merit

Conclusion

Self-Practice

Healing Practice for Others

Dedication of Merit

Conclusion

Self-Practice

There are two main ways in which Nejang Yoga can be integrated into one's life and practice: It can be practiced in its entirety as a daily or retreat yogic practice, or it can be used 'prescriptively' as a treatment for particular ailments or imbalances in the physical body or energies. When practiced in its entirety as a yogic regime, the practitioner assumes the basic posture, begins with the preliminary meditations and breathing exercises taught in this book, and then proceeds through all twenty four exercises in order, repeating each exercise three, seven or twenty one times depending on the amount of time available. Performing the practice in this way while focusing the mind and engaging in the proper breathing technique with retention is a wonderful way to train the body and breath (or energy) and to cultivate mental concentration and refined awareness. Over time the body will become more supple, the mind more clear and calm, and the energy will flow better in the channels resulting in many health-related and ultimately spiritual benefits. It is highly recommended that you memorize the sequence of exercises so that you can enter into a deeper meditative state of mind while performing them.

The second way to practice is to study the indications taught in this book and then focus on a small selection of exercises from the twenty four that target particular problems. For example, we learned that according to Tibetan Medicine the eyes are the 'flower' of the liver and therefore if one has an issue with the liver (or its counterpart the gallbladder), one might spend extra time repeating the second exercise in the series which trains the movement of the eyes. Likewise, since the ear is the 'flower' of the kidney, those who want to strengthen the function of the kidneys should focus on the first ear massaging exercise, and so on, repeating a single exercise for five or ten minutes. It is possible to simply repeat a single exercise many times during one's practice session, or to repeat a few related exercises in a sequence.

Healing Practice for Others

As a healthcare practitioner, it is possible to prescribe a few relevant movements from the sequence of twenty four in line with the particular needs of a patient. This avoids the possibility of patients becoming overwhelmed by having to remember many different protocols and allows them to engage in exercises that can directly benefit their condition without taking up too much of their time. Nejang Yoga can be very useful for prolonging the beneficial effects of a manual therapy treatment such as acupuncture or massage and can help to empower patients to take a proactive stance towards their own healing.

Although Nejang consists of twenty four specific exercises, it can also be practiced in a very freestyle way. Any place in the body that is experiencing a problem or pain can be the *né* that you then clean and purify (*jang*). Rubbing and massaging or mobilizing any part of the body while retaining the breath and maintaining awareness is its own kind of Nejang Yoga practice that can be very beneficial.

བསོད་ནམས་འདི་ཡིས་ཐམས་ཅད་གཟིགས་པ་ཉིད།
SONAM DIYI TAMCHE ZIGPA NYI
By this merit, may all-seeing Buddhahood itself

ཐོབ་ནས་ཉེས་པའི་དགྲ་རྣམས་ཕམ་བྱས་ཏེ།
TOBNE NYEPAY DRANAM PAM CHE TE
Be obtained, and may the enemy of all wrongdoings be vanquished

སྐྱེ་ག་ན་འཆིའི་རྦ་ཀློང་འཁྲུགས་པ་ཡི།
KYE GA NA CHI BALONG TRUKPA YI
May I save all beings from [drowning] in the turbulent
whirlpools of (re)birth, aging, sickness, and death

སྲིད་པའི་མཚོ་ལས་འགྲོ་བ་སྒྲོལ་བར་ཤོག །
SIPAY TSO LE DROWA DROLWAR SHOG
in the ocean of samsara!

Dedication of Merit

In the same way that we begin our practice with an altruistic motivation to benefit all beings, we conclude our meditation or yoga by dedicating the merit or positive virtue or energy generated from our practice. This is a simple way of sharing the benefits of our practice with others and allowing our efforts to serve a greater purpose. There are several different traditional prayers that can be recited to close the session such as the one included here on the opposite page, but as with the Four Immeasurables practice, what is important is to really contemplate the meaning and say the words from your heart or to find your own personalized prayer or visualization to dedicate your merit. Remembering that we and all beings are trapped in the suffering of samsara due to misunderstanding and wrong actions, we make an aspiration to free ourselves from our ignorance and to work to free all others. We can share any health or spiritual benefit that we received from this Nejang Yoga, large or small, with other beings in the present, future and even in the past, so that their pain can be reduced and so that we may progress along the path to enlightenment.

Appendices

24 Sacred Abodes

About the Author

Bibliography and References

24 Sacred Abodes

The Hevajra Tantra lists the twenty four places as:

1.	Jalandhara	13.	Arbuta
2.	Oddiyana	14.	Godavari
3.	Paurnagiri	15.	Himadri
4.	Kamarupa	16.	Harikela
5.	Malaya	17.	Lampaka
6.	Sindhu	18.	Kani
7.	Nagara	19.	Saurasta
8.	Munmuni	20.	Kalinga
9.	Karunyapataka	21.	Kokana
10.	Devikota	22.	Caritra
11.	Karmarapataka	23.	Kosala
12.	Kulata	24.	Vindhyakaumarapaurika

The Chakrasamvara Tantra offers a similar,
but somewhat different list:

These twenty four locations correspond to the Shakti Pithas, important pilgrimage sites sacred to Shaivites, which are revered as different parts of the body of the great cosmic Goddess[19].

1.	Pulliramalaya	13.	Kalinga
2.	Jalandhara	14.	Lambaka
3.	Oddiyana	15.	Kanchi
4.	Arbuta	16.	Himalaya
5.	Godavari	17.	Pretapuri
6.	Rameshavara	18.	Grihadeva
7.	Devikoti	19.	Saurashta
8.	Malawa	20.	Suvarnadvipa
9.	Kamarupa	21.	Nagara
10.	Ote	22.	Sindhura
11.	Trisakune	23.	Maro
12.	Kosala	24.	Kuluta

Also very relevant for our topic of Nejang Yoga, though not an exact correlation to each of the body parts worked in our practice, is the description of the twenty four places that is found in the *Longchen Nyingthig* Sadhana, the "Queen of Great Bliss" *(Yumka Dechen Gyalmo)*. This practice text, which was revealed through visions by the Tibetan tantric Buddhist master Jigme Lingpa (1730 - 1798), describes the twenty four sacred places as locations within the perfected body of the wrathful red *dakini* or female tantric Buddha Vajravarahi (the *sambkogakaya* emanation of Vajrayogini), which in turn exist within the subtle vajra anatomy of every sentient being.

In the sadhana the twenty four places are divided into three groups:

Eight celestial abodes:

1) Crown of the head: Jalandhara
2) In between the eyebrows: Pulliramalaya,
3) Nape: Arbuta
4) Urna (the hair at the center of the forehead) is Rameshvara
5) Right ear: Oddiyana
6) Left ear: Godavari [Lapchi]
7) Eyes: Devikota [Tsari]
8) Shoulders: Malava.

19. Shabkar Tsogdruk Rangdrol, *The Life of Shabkar* (Albany: SUNY Press, 1994), 342.

Eight earthly abodes:

9) Throat: Lampaka
10) Underarms and kidneys: Kamarupa
11) Breasts: Odra
12) Navel: Trishanku
13) Tip of the nose: is Koshala
14) Palate: Kalinga
15) Heart: Kanchika*
16) Heart: Himalaya (Himavat) [Mt. Kailash]*
    (*The heart is associated with two locations in this sadhana.)

Eight undergound abodes:

17) Genitals: Pretapuri
18) Anus: Grihadeva
19) Thumbs and big toes: Maru
20) Thighs: Saurashtra
21) Calves: Suvarnadvipa
22) The sixteen other fingers and toes: Nagara
23) Knees: Kulata
24) Ankles: Sindhu.

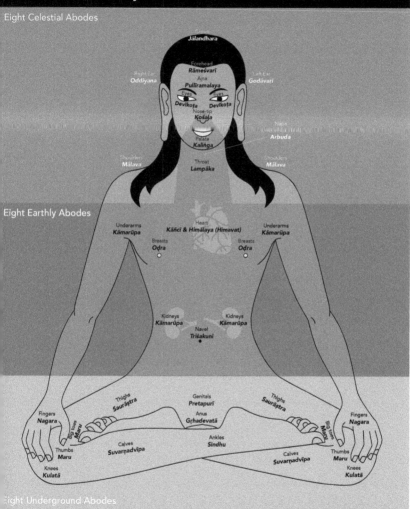

Twenty Four Great Sacred Places

Eight Celestial Abodes

Jālandhara

Forehead
Rāmeśvarī

Right Ear
Oḍḍiyāna

Ajna
Pulliramalaya

Left Ear
Godāvarī

Eyes
Devīkoṭa

Eyes
Devīkoṭa

Nose-tip
Kośala

Nape
Arbuda

Palate
Kaliṅga

Shoulders
Mālava

Throat
Lampāka

Shoulders
Mālava

Eight Earthly Abodes

Underarms
Kāmarūpa

Heart
Kāñcī & Himālaya (Himavat)

Underarms
Kāmarūpa

Breasts
Oḍra

Breasts
Oḍra

Kidneys
Kāmarūpa

Kidneys
Kāmarūpa

Navel
Triśakuni

Fingers
Nagara

Thighs
Saurāṣṭra

Genitals
Pretapurī

Thighs
Saurāṣṭra

Fingers
Nagara

Big toes
Maru

Anus
Gṛhadevatā

Big toes
Maru

Thumbs
Maru

Calves
Suvarṇadvīpa

Ankles
Sindhu

Calves
Suvarṇadvīpa

Thumbs
Maru

Knees
Kulatā

Knees
Kulatā

Eight Underground Abodes

About the Author

Dr. Nida Chenagtsang was born in Amdo, in North Eastern Tibet. Interested in Sowa Rigpa, the traditional healing science of his people, he began his early medical studies at the local Tibetan Medicine hospital. Later he was awarded a scholarship to enter the Lhasa Tibetan Medical University where he completed his medical education in 1996, with practical training at the Tibetan Medicine hospitals in Lhasa and Lhoka. Alongside his medical education, Dr. Nida received comprehensive Vajrayana Buddhist training in the Longchen Nyingthig and Dudjom Tersar traditions and trained in the Yuthok Nyingthig lineage, the spiritual healing tradition and esoteric component of Sowa Rigpa, with his teachers Khenchen Troru Tsenam and Khenpo Tsultrim Gyaltsen.

Dr. Nida has published many articles and books on Sowa Rigpa and the Yuthok Nyingthig tradition. He has extensively researched ancient Tibetan healing methods, and has gained great acclaim in both the East and the West for his revival of traditional Tibetan external healing therapies.

Dr. Nida is the Co-Founder and Medical Director of Sorig Khang International (**sorig.net**) with branch centers in over forty countries worldwide and Co-Founder and Medical and Spiritual Director of the Sorig Institute (**www.soriginstute.org**) and Pure Land Farms (**www.purelandfarms.org**), Centers for Tibetan Medicine, Meditation and Rejuvenation based in the Los Angeles, California.

To learn more about Dr. Nida's teaching activities and how to train in Nejang Yoga with qualified teachers in your country, please visit **www.sorig.net**.

Bibliography and References

Baker, Ian. *The Heart of the World: A Journey to Tibet's Lost Paradise.* London: Penguin Books, 2004.

Tibetan Yoga: Principles and Practice. Rochester: Inner Traditions, 2019.

Bryant, Edwin F. *The Yoga Sūtras of Patañjali: A New Edition, Translation, and Commentary.* New York: North Point Press, 2009.

Chenagtsang, Nida. *Mirror of Light: A Commentary on Yuthok's Ati Yoga, Volume One.* Translated by Ben Joffe. Portland: Sky Press, 2016.

The Tibetan Book of Health: Sowa Rigpa, the Science of Healing. Portland: Sky Press, 2017.

Weapon of Light: Introduction to Ati Yoga Meditation. Portland: SKY Press, 2017.

Karmamudra: The Yoga of Bliss – Sexuality in Tibetan Medicine and Buddhism. Portland: SKY Press, 2018.

Chenagtsang, Nida and Tam Nguyen. *Sowa Rigpa Points: Point Study in Traditional Tibetan Medicine.* Portland: Sky Press, 2017.

Gönpo, Yuthok Yönten. *The Basic Tantra and The Explanatory Tantra from the Secret Quintessential Instructions of the Eight Branches of the Ambrosia Essence Tantra.*
Dharamsala: Men-Tsee-Khang Publications, 2008.

Gray, David B. *The Cakrasamvara Tantra (The Discourse of Śrī Heruka): A Study and Annotated Translation.* New York: American Institution of Buddhist Studies (Columbia University), 2007.

Pal, G.K., S. Velkumary, and Madanmohan. *"Effect of short-term practice of breathing exercises on autonomic functions in normal human volunteers."* Indian Journal of Medical Research. Vol. 120, Iss. 2 (Aug. 2004): 115-121.

Shabkar Tsogdruk Rangdrol. *The Life of Shabkar: The Autobiography of a Tibetan Yogin.* Translated by Matthieu Ricard (1st paperback edition). Albany: SUNY Press, 1994.

Snellgrove, David. *The Hevajra Tantra: A Critical Study.* Bangkok: Orchid Press, 2011.

Thurman, Robert and Tad Wise. *Circling the Sacred Mountain: A Spiritual Adventure Through the Himalayas.* New York: Bantam Books, 1999.

Zangpo, Ngawang. *Sacred Ground: Jamgon Kongtrul on Pilgrimage and Sacred Geography.* Ithaca, N.Y.: Snow Lion, 2001.

Tibetan works cited:

Butön Rinchen Drup (Bu ston rin chen grub). "Sbyor ba yan lag drug gi 'phrul 'khor" ["The Magic Wheel Trulkhor Exercises of the Six-Limbed Yoga"]. In *Gsang chen thabs lam nyer mkho rnal 'byor snying nor.* Vol. 1, 195 – 203. Beijing: Mi rigs dpe skrun khang, 1991.

Jigme Lingpa ('jigs med gling pa)/Lotsawa House. "Yumka Dechen Gyalmo – Tibetan" (yum ka mtsho rgyal bde chen rgyal mo'i rtsa ba'i sgrub pa bde chen dpal phreng). Accessed January 14, 2020. https://www.lotsawahouse.org/bo/tibetan-masters/jigme-lingpa/yumka-dechen-gyalmo-sadhana

Saraha (Sa ra ha). "Do ha mdzod kyi glu" ['Songs from the Treasury of Songs of Realization']. In Bstan *'gyur dpe bsdur ma* [The Comparative edition Tengyur, the collection of translated Buddhist commentaries]. Beijing: Krung go'i bod rig pa'i dpe skrun khang, 1994 – 2008, Vol. 26, 193 – 210.

Sakya Pandita Kunga Gyaltsen (Sa skya pan di ta kun dga' rgyal mtshan)/ Lotsawa House. "Aspiration to Recite While Prostrating – Tibetan" (phyag 'tshal skabs 'don rgyu'i smon tshig). Accessed January 10, 2020. https://www.lotsawahouse.org/bo/tibetan-masters/sakya-pandita/aspiration-while-prostrating

Lightning Source UK Ltd.
Milton Keynes UK
UKHW021100110520
363093UK00006B/755